3 1336 00153 5625

D0466947

A HISTORY OF PSYCHIATRY

A HISTORY OF PSYCHIATRY

By

JEROME M. SCHNECK, A.B., M.D.

Clinical Associate Professor of Psychiatry

State University of New York College of Medicine

New York City

CHARLES C THOMAS · PUBLISHER

Springfield · Illinois · U.S.A.

CHARLES C THOMAS · PUBLISHER
BANNERSTONE HOUSE
301-327 East Lawrence Avenue, Springfield, Illinois, U.S.A.

Published simultaneously in the British Commonwealth of Nations by
BLACKWELL SCIENTIFIC PUBLICATIONS, LTD., OXFORD, ENGLAND

Published simultaneously in Canada by
THE RYERSON PRESS, TORONTO

Library of Congress Catalog Card Number: 59-14209

With THOMAS BOOKS careful attention is given to all details of manufacturing and design. It is the Publisher's desire to present books that are satisfactory as to their physical qualities and artistic possibilities and appropriate for their particular use. THOMAS BOOKS will be true to those laws of quality that assure a good name and good will.

Printed in the United States of America

To the Memory of my Father

MAURICE SCHNECK, M.D.

PREFACE

Departments of psychiatry in medical schools have expanded greatly during the past two decades. Medical educators agree generally on the importance of historical perspective in all branches of study. I should like this book to enhance this perspective for students during their courses as undergraduates, and I desire also to furnish a compact, up to date, readable volume for young physicians in their intensive postgraduate studies preparing them for active practice and general participation in the specialty of psychiatry.

This work is written from the vantage point of the clinician. For highly detailed treatises of greater magnitude suitable for scholarly or encyclopedic reference, other books are available. Practicing psychiatrists and others concerned with the social and behavioral sciences who may wish to renew and replenish their acquaintance with fascinating backgrounds of psychiatric endeavor, will find the opportunity through these pages.

The general outline of this history follows a chronological sequence. For specific time periods, however, there has been no rigid adherence to this form. Flexibility is necessary on this score in order to present satisfactorily certain meaningful but scattered happenings that are part of fundamental dynamic developments.

I have not limited this volume to presentation of the main currents of thought and activity in medical psychology and psychiatry as described by others before me. The special feature in this effort has been the selection of new historical researches, opinions, and interpretations from recent publications in professional journals and their integration into discussions of major historical trends and achievements. Toward this end I have searched the literature carefully and have found clinical journals to be a rich and fruitful source of historical materials. They are, without doubt, a significant supplement to the traditional supplies of medico-historical bulletins.

I am much indebted to the writings of others in the development of this book. Gregory Zilboorg and Nolan D. C. Lewis must be noted for their histories of medical psychology and psychiatry. Erwin H. Ackerknecht and Henry E. Sigerist deserve special mention for backgrounds of general medicine. The late Doctor Sigerist has long been an inspiration in furthering my appreciation of the historical point of view. The influence on this work of the books and articles by many contributors is apparent, but their names are too numerous to mention here. The reader will find, however, that proper acknowledgment is granted to all who have been of help, and they are identified in the text or in the references. My opinions and points of view, and what I have brought to bear on this account from my own clinical experience, are items for which I clearly assume personal responsibility.

JEROME M. SCHNECK, M.D.

CONTENTS

A HISTORY OF PSYCHIATRY

Chapter 1

PRIMITIVE SOCIETIES AND ARCHAIC MEDICINE

For primitive groups, concepts of disease incorporate the influence of spirits and power of offended gods. Their ideas about most forms of illness probably entail such views. The approach to sickness is magico-religious, and supernaturalism pervades these cultures. In all primitive societies similar ideas may be discovered regarding the causes of disease (1). The violation of a taboo is a potent psychological force. As Zilboorg, the historian of psychiatry, has intimated, primitive man's world of spirits is a reflection of his anxieties (2). Most of us would agree, however, that we know little about primitive "psychiatry." When evaluating primitive groups and cultures, one may wish to heed the terms used by the medical historian, Ackerknecht (1). For him, "paleomedicine" pertains to ancient man; "primitive medicine," to contemporary tribes. Relatively little is known about the latter and far less about the former.

Primitive man makes no distinction, apparently, between disease that we are accustomed to designate physical and mental. In one view, it is all mental for him in the sense of spiritistic (2). It may be transmitted by sorcerers. The supernaturalistic orientation is basic. Yet, while we falter over terms and classifications in today's "scientific" medicine, and as we grope toward a holistic concept of man and his functioning, primitives see one disease and its treatment. This unitary feature has been regarded as a predominant element in primitive medicine (1). Physical measures and psychological approaches are therapeutically entwined. Sigerist, the distinguished physician-historian, ventured to state that indeed for these cultures, magic, religion, and medicine are one (3).

Sir James Frazer described the Law of Similarity and the Law of Contact or Contagion (4). Like produces like, hence an effect resembles its cause. Things once in contact continue to interact even at a distance after contact has been severed. Charms relating to the Law of Similarity are part of Homeopathic or Imitative Magic. When related to the Law of Contact they are Contagious Magic. An assertion by Frazer is of particular relevance to medical psychology and psychopathology. This is the claim that the primitive magician does not analyze the mental processes in his magical practice. He does not dwell on the abstract principles. Thus, magic can be only an art, never a science. Yet it is probably true that the separation of contemporary science and magic is not as decisive as Frazer might indicate. Likewise, based on studies of comparative religion, it would seem that magic in one culture may possess the status of religion in another (5).

It has been stated that homeopathic magic may be used alone but contagious magic usually involves imitative magic (4). One of the most widely known applications of a magic principle is the attempt to harm an enemy by damaging an image of him. This may kill or induce illness. It is surely remarkable though not surprising that an intense belief of this type may produce psychological reactions so vital that sickness with psychological and physiological manifestations may result. Yet this odd and alien happening surely has its counterpart in contemporary, so-called civilized groups where intense psychological pressures and conflictual interpersonal relations foster guilt, remorse, anxiety, and their consequences in disruption of healthy functioning.

Homeopathic magic may be used with constructive intent. Often described is the curious practice for women in labor among the Dyaks of Borneo (4). The healer may play the role of the parturient woman, lie nearby with a stone attached to his abdomen, and move about in representation of the birth experience until this symbolic equivalent of the unborn child is finally removed from him. This curious type of active participation by the healer or his assistants is found in other types of cases with fascinating psychological implications or involvements, some of which are obvious and others of which may be conjectured. For example, Ackerknecht (6) has referred to the medicine-man, acting in good faith, starting treatment by entering a state of trance or "possession." The prototype of this possessed medicine-man is the Siberian shaman. It has been pointed out that descriptions of such performances as miraculous and suggestive may, if limited to this alone, lend an impression of superficiality to the evaluations. The effectiveness of treatment in such a setting may be based in part on the ability of the patient to identify himself with the healer within the framework of conscious acceptance of social and religious beliefs pertaining to this treatment or through his unconscious evaluation and interpretation of the medical procedure (Schneck, 7). A patient as product of the same culture as his medicine-man may reasonably follow through his identification to the experience of entering a state of death with which the trance state is at times equated, and then emerging from it as a process of being reborn. The patient would have his experience vicariously through identification with the trance of his healer.

Frazer (4) has referred to some trances among primitives as "death-like" and has claimed that for some groups this state is hardly distinguished from death. Rose (8) has described some rituals centering around the experience of death and the power to pass through its confines. In some areas the setting is described as trance and interpreted as such, whereas in others the trance experience is referred to as death. These curious rites and beliefs are not so far removed from contemporary western thought as one might suppose. Only recently has clinical therapeutic experience demonstrated that, for at least some people, hypnosis and death, and hypnosis and rebirth are apparently equated unconsciously (Schneck, 9). It has been suggested too that these identifications may be involved, more than is realized as yet, with widespread belief regarding remarkable beneficial effects of hypnotic procedure consisting of simple, authoritative suggestion.

The state of trance need not be involved for identifications with death and rebirth experience. In illustration of homeopathic magic, the Dyak medicine-man may simply lie down and pretend to be dead (4). He is treated like a corpse, placed in mats, and removed from the home of his patient. His assistants unbind him later and recovery of the ill person is supposed to be effected through the return of his healer to life. Among the Loango in French Equatorial Africa, the diviner may enter a trance at night, whereupon his soul departs to consult ancestral spirits. On its return, he knows whether the illness is to be ascribed to a wizard, a fetish, or taboo violation (3).

Although trance states are involved only in certain types of magico-religious medicine, they are encountered frequently. Evidently they are essentially the hypnotic trance experiences known today in occidental settings. This sameness pertains to Siberian tribes, to Cochin China, and to parts of the Malay Archipelago according to Zilboorg (2). At times the descriptions of procedure as hypnotic is questionable, but on occasion the accounts are precise and beyond doubt. A recent example pertains to such use of a "magic stone" by a clever man of Tabulum (New South Wales). This object was used for focussing attention of the individual in whom a trance was to be induced, and the method is actually what would be called in current scientific literature the ocular or visual fixation technique. Its principle use in the Tabulum setting was said to be for instruction of young initiates. The rites engaged in may also incorporate a form of traveling clairvoyance. This and related experiences encountered in types of magico-religious functions and procedures of primitive medicine fall into areas within the province of contemporary parapsychological interests and investigations (8, 10). The role of trance among primitive peoples has been described often (11). The loss of the soul as significant in the causation of disease has also been alluded to frequently. It has been encountered in Siberia, among Eskimos, in Polynesia and Melanesia, and among American Indians of the Northwest (3). In the healing process the medicine-man must find the lost soul and return it to the body of his patient. To achieve this, the Siberian shaman consults his guardian spirits and learns what is wrong. During the rites he beats a drum, sings, and dances in a frenzy. He has, as mentioned before, been described as the prototype of the possessed medicine-man (6). Ackerknecht regards the trance as normal possession of the medicine-man, whereas pathological possession is the prototype of a mental disease in which suggestion plays a role. An example usually supplied is Latah, the Malayan name of an illness found among Indonesians and Siberians (6). It consists of compulsive imitative movements and verbalizations.

Possession has also been termed latent or overt depending on its manifestations (12). It is overt when the possessing spirit actually speaks through the possessed. It is latent when the possessed is not aware of the spirit within him. In the latter case, according to Ellenberger, symptoms of mental illness manifest themselves without the possessed being aware of his victimization by the evil spirit. By forcing the spirit to speak out in cases of latent possession, the exorcist can begin to effect a cure. Exorcism has been called a well structured type of psychotherapy characterized usually by the exorcist speaking in the name of a higher force rather than in his own, having complete faith in the higher being, and accepting the reality of possession and of the spirit involved. This spirit is contacted seriously, the patient is encouraged, and preparation of the exorcist for his total task is laborious. It may involve prayer and fasting. The structure of this type of phenomenon and the relationships between the persons concerned does vary in different areas and at different times but the essential ingredients are similar (12). Exorcism is regarded as one of the oldest types of psychotherapy.

Primitive medicine-men may receive extensive schooling in their highly specialized activities. In illustration one may examine the case among the Kwakiutl Indians, studied and reported by anthropologist Franz Boas (13). The shamans among them take a four year study period under established rules, learning a specialized professional program. Secrecy has a place of importance in the organizational framework. There are rival shamanistic schools with variations in techniques and conflicting claims among them of greater superiority in methods (12). One may see clearly some similarities to vocal contemporary schools of psychotherapy.

An attempt may be made at times to fathom the dynamics of some primitive customs in terms of current theoretical views. The helpfulness of interpretations would obviously depend on one's point of view. Frazer told of people in the Babar Archipelago striking themselves with stones with the aim of transferring to these stones the fatigue which they experienced (4). To the extent that such fatigue might be an expression of psychological conflict probably incorporating feelings of guilt, this act might be effective at times in supplying relief through self-punishment. There is, of course, identification of this act with social acceptability. The rite involves discarding the stones in specially designated places. Another example may relate to the link between certain types of headache and the repression of hostility. A Moor suffering from headaches is said to take a lamb or goat, at times, and beat it severely in the belief that the headache will be transferred to the animal (4). As a means of externalizing troublesome aggressive feelings in ritualistic fashion, such an act may well be effective at least temporarily. Categorizing such behavior for primitives, Frazer speaks of the transference of evil. He has also described patients being struck in the face with certain leaves which are then thrown away. This is said to be the cure for epilepsy in some East Indian islands. The disease passes to the leaves and is thereby eliminated. It might be suspected that psychogenic seizures would be selectively responsive on occasion.

Of endless interest are the trephined skulls available as remnants of protohistoric times and evidences of paleomedicine. Paul Broca (1824-1880) was much interested in the anatomical findings and the surgical techniques. This distinguished surgeon-anthropologist is said to be the first to have studied such skulls, and their significance is regarded as still unsettled (1). Broca, a student of cerebral localization, is credited also with a significant role in placing brain surgery on a scientific plane (14). As for the trephined skulls, he favored the view that the purpose in this procedure was to liberate evil spirits responsible for headaches or epilepsy. An opposing opinion supported the idea that the operation of trepanation was to remove bone fragments and decrease intracranial pressure. This belief was based on the claim that the bone surgery occurred mostly in areas where weapons of a type that could produce skull fractures had been in use (1). The fact that excised rondelles were employed as amulets was considered a point in favor of Broca's impressions. Ackerknecht has taken these views into consideration and notes that both the supernaturalistic and naturalistic approaches have been observed, and that it is important to see trepanation as a peculiarly limited achievement of primitives who are poor surgeons in other respects. Since it is secret procedure in areas such as the Andean highlands, he suggests reinforcement of its basis in supernaturalistic lore. In relation to primitive man's concern with spirits as reflections of his own anxiety, Zilboorg has indicated that his efforts were directed more toward eliminating fear incurred by illness than toward realistic attempts to remove the illness itself. The question that still remains is what one would regard as realistic, for even at present there are persistent claims and counterclaims on this score within the practice of contemporary medicine. Within psychiatric practice specifically these differences of opinion exist, for example, in regard to physical and psychological treatment approaches. A case in point is the basis of behavioral change following electroshock therapy and psychoanalytic therapy about which there are opposing and contradictory views.

An important part of medical tradition among primitive groups is the use of spells or incantations, frequently offered repetitiously, and often consisting of songs. Magic formulas and incantations could be used alone or in conjunction with physical administrations. These psychotherapeutic rites might be delivered in a sacred language understood only by the medicine-men, not the patients or the general population (6). Drugs may be incorporated into treatment among many primitive peoples and some of these are also in use in scientific medicine. Yet many medicine-men have no knowledge of drugs. Others use them indiscriminately and at least one historian has indicated that they may serve as psychotherapeutic agents in this way (6). This point is of interest in view of current investigations of the psychotherapeutic aspects of medications within the framework of the doctor-patient relationship. Worthy of comment also is the existence of medical rites performed in silence, with its implied psychological significances as part of total therapy. Ackerknecht offers South American Indians as an example (6). The role of silence within the context of some current psychotherapeutic relationships is included among contemporary studies of interpersonal contacts and issues of non-verbal communication.

Many of the characteristics and practices of primitive medicine constitute a significant part of procedures in archaic societies. The wish to eliminate the anxiety related to illness, rather than to engage in realistic attempts to eliminate the basic illness, is mentioned by Zilboorg (2) as still having been evident in Egypt at the time of Imhotep, and centuries later too among other civilized countries. Imhotep, who died about 2850 B. C., was a high official, functioned as a physician while engaged in many legal and architectural works, was regarded as a demigod after his death, and was then considered a god many centuries later (14). Curiously, Imhotep, the Father of Egyptian Medicine, who has been described by Osler (15) as the first physician to emerge clearly from antiquity, apparently left no medical writings or group of disciples (14).

While interest in the world of medicine was stimulated considerably by findings in the Edwin Smith Papyrus and the Ebers Papyrus, the clinical insights revealed in them should not, it has been stated, obscure the view of extensive supernaturalism in Egyptian medicine (1). These writings refer to amulets and magic rites as well as hygienic principles. The worship of sacred animals continued to play an important role in controlling sickness and health, life and death. As Bromberg has indicated, the gradual movement in methods of healing from magic to faith and to science has involved progressions and retrogressions and their intermixtures (16). These intermixtures surely continue.

Amidst accounts of medical ministrations and actions of evil spirits, it has been possible, as Lewis has revealed, to discern in the Egyptian papyri representations of alcoholic reactions, senile deteriorations, melancholia, and hysterical reactions, the latter having been viewed as contagious at times (17). The variety of healing procedures in ancient Egyptian medical lore might involve oral rites consisting of simple or complex incantations, or manual rites and combinations of methods. One of the manual rites was the simple laying on of hands which is so well known as a persistent psychological force through the course of history. As in aforementioned aspects of primitive medicine, the Egyptians also used methods of sympathetic magic. Sigerist has aptly pointed out that sudden relief might indeed come about as a result of the psychological influence of incantations and manual rites in allaying anxiety. But he expressed the opinion too that most patients obtained no significant, lasting, sudden beneficial response (3). Many would want to retain the magic force, and consistent with what would be studied today in relation to dependency requirements and transference issues, objects would be imbued with magic power to be retained and to serve as amulet and talisman.

As was true of all civilizations at that time, Mesopotamian medicine existed under the dominating influence of religion. Whereas the beginnings of a division between magico-religious and empirico-rational medicine were discerned in Egypt, this never occurred in Mesopotamia, according to Sigerist, nor did he believe there was anything available from Mesopotamia comparable to the Edwin Smith Papyrus and portions of the Ebers Papyrus (3). Gods and goddesses were instrumental in the control of disease and health, court physicians were an organized group with hierarchy, and surgeons, exorcists, and diviners as well were of the priestly class (1). The Mesopotamians had systems of dream interpretation, and divination was highly developed. It was used for diagnosis where attempts to understand disease were made by discovering the sins that had been committed by the patient. There were prayers and spells, demons to be eliminated, gods to be appeased, and animal sacrifices to be offered. Physical therapies and drugs also had their place (18). Concepts of disease, uncleanliness, sin, and its punishment were so entwined, that we are told they could at times be referred to by the same terms (1).

Although it has been stated that among the ancient Hebrews social and personal hygienic customs made an imprint, at least indirectly on mental and physical health (16), hostility existed toward those afflicted with neuroses and psychoses (2). Mental illness was observed and clinical pictures emerged. They found their way into Biblical writings. Macht has dwelt on a variety of allusions pertaining to psychosomatic reactions, especially in the Books of Job, Ecclesiastes and Proverbs. As for the latter, he discerns considerable insights into personality functioning with the belief that observations correlate well with modern experimental findings and clinical data (19). Mania, depression, and other states of emotional disturbance experienced by various Biblical characters are often mentioned (2, 17).

Early medicine in India followed the trend of healing in primitive and archaic cultures. Spells and incantations formed part of the picture with exorcism, confession, and the importance of sin. Four holy Sanskrit books, the Vedas, contained the core of the healing rites and devices. The Vedic period has been designated as lasting until 800 B. C., followed by the Brahmanic period extending approximately to 1000 A. D. according to Ackerknecht (1). While the psychiatric content of the Vedas has not been deemed impressive, Lewis notes that in some parts there are indications of the first classification of disturbed mental functioning (17). Based on a core concept of demoniacal possession, he cites the five angers of devils, one of the gods, and one anger of spirits of dead men. Possession by these angers produces mental disease. Psychotic reactions are discernible in some descriptions of disorder. Convulsive seizures were in evidence as might be surmised, and there were observations of confusional states associated with ingestion of poison drugs. Although considerate attitudes toward the mentally ill are credited to the ancient Hindu healers, it is believed that a more formal type of deliberate psychotherapy did not arise until Greek medicine entered the scene (16). Yet similarities of Hindu medical psychology to the Greek have been pointed out, such as the soul inhabiting the heart, finding expression through parts of the body, and possessing qualities akin to our concepts of perception, intelligence and consciousness. Zilboorg sees *prana* as reminiscent of the *pneuma* among the Greeks (2). Of interest is the view that in the era of Susruta and Charaka there seemed to be no conflict between science and theology, an issue which is recurrent and is being reassessed now. Furthermore, Susruta has been seen as additionally advanced to the degree of suggesting psychopathology of nineteenth and twentieth century vintage through an awareness of the role of powerful emotions not only in mental illness but in the emergence of somatic problems that might even require surgical help (2). This type of forecasting may be discerned through the ages to some degree in many cultures. How far ahead of their times Susruta and Charaka may have been presents some difficulties too, because Major (14) reveals that various dates have been ascribed to the lives of these giants of Hindu medicine. Indeed some of the dates are centuries apart, preceding and following onset of the Christian era.

Demoniacal possession played a significant role in the beliefs of the ancient Chinese, and healing efforts involved priests and sorcerers. Thus, similarities to the early cultures already mentioned would apply here too, with stress on divination, incantation, and magic herbs (14). Lewis is of the opinion that early Chinese and Japanese writings furnish little of psychiatric importance (17). Medicine was bound closely with religion in Mexican healing measures, as in Egypt and Mesopotamia (1). Many of the approaches to sickness and health which have been described for the several archaic cultures apply once again. Astrological diagnosis was part of the pattern. As for possession, its place of importance in magico-religious medicine has been noted in numerous geographical areas (12). Listing of the many places and noting of details would be repetitious and superfluous. A final word may be offered, however, about ancient Peruvian medicine (20). The surgeons were skilled at trephining, and medical practice was allied to religion. Additional surgical procedures, moreover, included excision of tumors, amputation of limbs, and the replacement of these limbs with prosthetic devices. The surgeons also opened inflamed sinuses. Of particular interest is the description of use of guinea pigs in diagnosis. They were held over the patient to absorb the disease-producing elements, and then killed for examination to assist in diagnosis. This transference of illness has appeared in various forms through the years. In the late nineteenth century, magnets were used to transfer illness from one patient to another in studies of psychological disability, especially hysterical reactions. The technique has been ascribed to Babinski (21).

The main features of primitive and archaic medicine have been surveyed with particular reference to psychological aspects. With this background a transition is made now to thought and healing among the Greeks who are generally credited with the first significant movement toward viewing mental disorder from what is regarded as a more scientific basis.

REFERENCES

1. Ackerknecht, E. H.: *A Short History of Medicine.* New York, Ronald Press, 1955.
2. Zilboorg, G. and Henry, G. W.: *A History of Medical Psychology.* New York, W. W. Norton, 1941.
3. Sigerist, H. E.: *A History of Medicine,* Vol. 1, Primitive and Archaic Medicine. New York, Oxford University Press, 1951.
4. Frazer, J. G.: *The Golden Bough.* New York, Macmillan, 1922.
5. Ehrenwald, J.: *From Medicine Man to Freud.* New York, Dell, 1956.
6. Ackerknecht, E. H.: *"Mesmerism" in Primitive Societies. Ciba*

Symp., *9*:826, 1948.

7. Schneck, J. M.: The Hypnotic Trance, Magico-Religious Medicine, and Primitive Initiation Rites. *Psychoanal. Rev.*, *41*:182, 1954.
8. Rose, R.: Psi and Australian Aboriginals. *J. Am. Soc. Psychical Res.*, *46*:17, 1952.
9. Schneck, J. M.: Hypnosis-Death and Hypnosis-Rebirth Concepts in Relation to Hypnosis Theory. *J. Clin. Exper. Hyp.*, *3*:40, 1955.
10. Elkin, A. P.: *Aboriginal Men of High Degree.* Sydney, Australasian, 1945.
11. Benedict, R.: *Patterns of Culture.* New York, Penguin, 1947.
12. Ellenberger, H.: The Ancestry of Dynamic Psychotherapy. *Bull. Menninger Clin.*, *20*:288, 1956.
13. Boas, F.: *The Religion of the Kwakiutl Indians.* New York, Columbia University Press, 1932.
14. Major, R. H.: *A History of Medicine.* Springfield, Thomas, 1954.
15. Osler, W.: *The Evolution of Modern Medicine.* New Haven, Yale University Press, 1921.
16. Bromberg, W.: *Man Above Humanity.* Philadelphia, J. B. Lippincott, 1954.
17. Lewis, N. D. C.: *A Short History of Psychiatric Achievement.* London, Chapman and Hall, 1942.
18. Bender, G. A.: *A History of Medicine in Pictures* (The Code of Hammurabi). Therap. Notes 64 (No. 3), 1957.
19. Macht, D. I.: Psychosomatic Allusions in the Book of Proverbs. *Bull. Hist. Med.*, *18*:301, 1945.
20. Bender, G. A.: *A History of Medicine in Pictures* (Trephining in Ancient Peru). Therap. Notes 64 (No. 5), 1957.
21. Foveau De Courmelles, F. V.: *Hypnotism.* London, George Routledge and Sons, 1891.

Chapter 2

THE CONTRIBUTIONS OF ANCIENT GREECE AND ROME

According to Drabkin, two different attitudes toward psychological abnormality are evident in classical antiquity (1). One view is found readily in Greek literature dating from Homer. Many aspects of abnormal behavior were described, and aberrant functioning was traditionally imbued with supernatural implications and ascribed to the intervention of supernatural agencies. Such beliefs were basically a part of popular thinking. The other view was espoused in medical thinking and medical writings. Supernaturalism was cast aside and divine influence by-passed in attempts to explain causation of disease and the phenomena encountered. While the influence of the gods might guide the course of human events, illness was seen increasingly as naturalistic. The division between these outlooks was, we might imagine, not always quite precise. While Greek medicine had more in common with present day views than other ancient forms of practice, there were alterations within it, as could be expected, because it spanned about one thousand years. Furthermore, it has been affirmed that religious medicine was not only existent in ancient Greece, but that it was prominent in the beginnings. In addition, the physicians who ministered to the upper classes were able to retain their religious views but separated them from the practice of a more rational medicine (2). Mental disturbance was seen increasingly as a disease, and its manifestations as symptoms of disease, with attempts at naturalistic explanation consistent with attitudes toward disease in general. The trend was toward emphasis on physiological malfunctioning, with growing awareness of the brain as the organ for special attention. There appeared to be recognition of varieties of psychological problems that would involve a number of categories in current classifications (1). Another way of expressing the psychiatric trend of that time is to see the encompassment of psychopathology by medicine as countering more and more the obstacles of abstract philosophy and theurgic mysticism in Greek thought and culture (3). This approach implies virtually a battle for the healing role without a friendly welcome, and this thought is regarded by Zilboorg as notably impressive when evaluating the place of Hippocrates in the inclusion of psychiatric issues into medicine.

Hippocrates had predecessors about whom some facts should be mentioned. Their philosophical bent did not find quite the same place with him, and his interests were more restricted to medical practice (4). Pythagoras (c. 570-489 B. C.), for example, was concerned much with mathematics. His views were both scientific and mystical. Seeing life as composed of the elements earth, air, fire, and water, with his four humors in addition, blood, phlegm, yellow bile and black bile, supplied a humoral view of medicine which was of special influence until the concepts of Virchow assumed a place of importance during the nineteenth century (22). Consistent with his preoccupation with numbers, he is credited with the doctrine of critical days, according to Major, and Lewis remarks on the claim of his having been the first to credit the brain as the center of the intellect and mental disease as a disorder of the brain (5). These ideas were shared by his pupil, Alkmaeon (c. 500 B. C.) who has been called the first known medical author in Greece (4). Alkmaeon dissected animals, is said to have discovered the optic nerves, and advanced the belief that mental patients were amenable to reason (5). His contemporary, Anaxagoras (500-428 B. C.), is mentioned by Lewis (5) as having described the lateral ventricles of the brain, affirming this location as the residence of the soul. In opposition to Alkmaeon, Empedocles (c. 500-430 B. C.) viewed the heart as the center of consciousness. Regarded as a skilled physician (4), Empedocles has been joined with Heraclitus as pre-Socratic philosophers reflecting analogies with Freud and Jung as theorists. The historical integration stressed has to do with the concern about opposing forces within the universe and the individual, and the persistent theme of opposites as a cosmological issue or a psychological expression of significant aspects of personality functioning (6).

There are many points of general medical interest about Hippocrates whose influence has lasted for centuries, and points also of special interest in connection with the history of psychiatry. He was the son of a physician and is believed to have lived about 460 to 377 B. C. Whereas some of his writings are part of what is known as the *Corpus Hippocraticum,* this work includes material prepared by others. Differentiation has been difficult if not impossible. The works were grouped together at Alexandria in the third century B. C. The individual items vary considerably in length, and contain some contradictory statements but have much in common (2). The general influence of Hippocrates as the Father of Medicine has been summarized by Roddis (7). He fostered the separation of medicine from philosophy and theology with the often mentioned view of illness as a natural process moving toward recovery, chronicity, or death. He stressed practice as a means of assisting nature and stimulated an observational approach in clinical medicine. He devised an oath which has served for centuries as a guide to ethical behavior (8).

It is frequently mentioned that Hippocrates was more interested in the total patient than in any specially designated diseased part. This point has current appeal because of stress on the holistic approach in medicine. Another item of reference is to Hippocrates' concern with treatment and prognosis rather than diagnosis (2). In later years, with special relation to mental illness and the renowned Kraepelin, it was to be the link between diagnosis and prognosis with less emphasis on treatment. As for prognosis, an interesting note is offered by Veith (9). She points out that in Greece the physician depended on the good will of his patients for his livelihood and it was to them that he felt responsible. The opinion was expressed that in the Hippocratic work on prognostics, scientific concern was not alone the important issue. A significant consideration was to avoid mistakes, and capable prognostication was a means of achieving a reputation. Aside from the financial issue, however, the contribution was, of course, an advance in medicine at that time.

One of the best known opinions of Hippocrates has to do with his regarding epilepsy, the Sacred Disease, as similar to other illnesses considered by him as natural occurrences. He is credited with recognition of post-partum psychoses, phobic reactions, mental confusion after hemorrhage, and the deleria in tuberculosis and malaria (3). He discerned states of mania and melancholia. Although some of the terms used are the same or similar to present usage, the meanings may differ at times. Zilboorg, for example, believes that his reference to paranoia suggests what would be considered now as a process of mental deterioration. On the other hand, the separations may not be too precise in all instances. There have been problems with classifications through the years. Recently, Wall supplied a pertinent item (10). Melancholia has been observed carefully for centuries and the term is one of the oldest in medicine. He indicated that the present classical concept was clarified by Kraepelin when he was differentiating manic-depressive psychoses from dementia praecox. Later, in 1907, Dreyfus saw no reason to separate involutional melancholia from manic-depressive psychoses. Wall then quoted Kraepelin as accepting the latter view, resulting eventually in Kraepelin's original opinion continuing to be accepted in American psychiatry, with most European centers retaining the revised opinion combining the reaction types.

Hippocrates has been credited also with recognizing hysteria which he evaluated as a somatic problem involving women in whom the uterus wandered. Because he is said to have recommended marriage to overcome the affliction, some have chosen to regard Hippocrates as sensing intuitively, but not consciously, its sexual implications (3). This willingness to ascribe special insights to historical figures may be reasonably valid at times. It is, however, frequently overdone and in recent years especially there has been the tendency to see many lesser or greater innovators as discerning precursors of Freud.

When alluding to Hippocratic thought about heat, cold, moisture and dryness, with varying admixtures as integral factors in disease pathology, Lewis (5) referred also to Hippocrates as the first to stress heredity and predisposition in connection with mental disease. Some clinical accounts were believed also to describe cases of neurosyphilis. Mental illness was evaluated as mania, melancholia, and phrenitis. Lewis was also impressed by an awareness, at times, of a relationship between elation and depression, showing that Hippocrates was one of the earliest medical figures to observe this connection which was later crystalized in the researches of Kraepelin. The nosological pattern of Hippocrates was relatively simple. Through the years, psychiatric classification was to occupy the attention of many people and it was to undergo changes varying markedly in complexity. Only recently has there been stressed again the trend toward simplication. This has involved too a more holistic concept of mental illness. It was epitomized in the nineteenth century by Neumann, author of *Lehrbuch der Psychiatrie* (1859), when he declared the existence of but one mental disease. The unitary concept has been advocated by psychiatrists in recent years. Karl Menninger sees Pierre Janet's organic and functional groups as constituting essentially a unitarian point of view, and Adolf Meyer's reaction types in psychiatric classification are seen as basically part of a holistic approach in contrast to the Kraepelinian classifications (11).

The mania and melancholia mentioned by Lewis in connection with Hippocrates were, apparently and in line with ideas presented by Drabkin (1), somewhat chronic ailments without fever. Phrenitis was a primary, acute reaction characterized by fever and excitement. Its counterpart with depression was lethargus. It seems, however, that phrenitis and lethargus, mania and melancholia, were not always precisely defined and mixed characteristics were seen. This is not surprising and in fact is consistent with difficult problems encountered at present with psychiatric classifications. The mild forms of neuroses may have been unrecognized at times (1). Even so, the opinion has been offered that during the Hippocratic era the variety of reactions seen now were also clinically assessed. This includes phobic reactions, obssessive-compulsive problems, hypochondriacal complaints, and neurasthenia (5).

Hippocrates was aware of motor and sensory disturbances following head injury. Accepting the brain as the center of intellect, it was considered to be involved in dream life and of significance in the function of sleep. As for dreams themselves, they were related to divine will on the one hand, and the condition of the body on the other (5). Dream interpretation was a specialty, a point of fact within and outside of scientific circles then and now. Seeing the mind as continuing to function in sleep without outside interference, hence the production of dreams, Hippocrates has been evaluated, in keeping with a trend commented on earlier, as a forerunner of Freud. Since he also observed intercurrent somatic illness modifying the course of mental disease, he has been credited with intuition brought to fruition in more recent times in the development of malarial therapy for general paresis (3).

Zilboorg (3) sees the medical psychology of Hippocrates as mainly physiological. He stressed the role of the brain but did not imbue it with psychological attributes. The pneuma was the basis of intellect and feeling. Yet psychological factors were included in the evaluation of disease, aside from the anatomical and physiological. Emotional elements impinge on the humoral or physiological processes, according to this conception. The appearance of disease is influenced by constitutional factors (1). Climatic conditions also play a role, with the spring season linked to mania, melancholia, and epilepsy (3).

Great doctors of antiquity have been acclaimed psychotherapists too and Hippocrates has had a measure of this type of adulation (12). He is praised also as an expert in forensic medicine. Taking all aforementioned appraisals into consideration, it is worth noting that Zilboorg is willing to view him as having fostered the beginnings of medical psychology with little added by others for many years after (3).

Plato (427-347 B. C.) moved, in certain respects, counter to the Hippocratic tradition. For him, epilepsy was still the Sacred Disease. He considered the brain structure similar to bone marrow (5). The rational soul was located in the brain. The irrational soul was in the chest. His views have constituted, Zilboorg believes, a step backward in the history of psychology and a blow to the medical point of view developed by Hippocrates. This retrogression was intensified by virtue of Plato's considerable influence on succeeding generations (3).

In his historical evaluation of the development of psychology, Gardner Murphy has seen Aristotle (384-322 B. C.), Plato's pupil, as a man intent on studying the relationships between mental and physical processes, with an interest in distinguishing between them (13). He was concerned with natural phenomena and the unification of knowledge. While he has been credited with viewing psychological reactions as total reactions, we find a more antiquated rather than modern note in his designation of the heart as the center of sensations. There, images and memory are converted to thought (3). He was more allied to current trends in his observation of a continuum in psychological reactions without sharp separations between normal and pathological. Although he was a physician, his influence on medicine has been considered indirect (2). He is thought of as a great philosopher and biologist. Ackerknecht sees his imprint as not completely wholesome because of the deductive and teleological trends that appear in his writings. His stress on the role of the heart is seen additionally as having forestalled earlier understandings of brain physiology (2). Aristotle has been described as the first to have directed attention to the frequency of melancholia (5).

The importance of the brain in its central role for the nervous system was restated by Herophilus (335-280 B. C.). He was one of the earliest systematic anatomists (5). He has, in fact, been called the Father of Anatomy (4). Aside from his descriptions of many parts of the brain, he may have differentiated nerves from tendons but did, in any case, separate the former into sensory and motor groups. Also, he distinguished arteries from veins. The gap between the Hippocratic influence and the neurological advances of Herophilus and Erasistratus (310-250 B. C.) has been ascribed to the influence of Aristotle among others. It has been seen by Zilboorg as characteristic of a historical tendency for medicine to play a role in the development of psychiatry, only to lose ground to speculative philosophy (3). The medical historian, Charles Singer, remarks that Herophilus was probably the first to perform human dissections in public. Agreeing to the importance of Herophilus in the origins of the study of anatomy, Singer credits his younger contemporary, Erasistratus, an Alexandrian like Herophilus, as the Father of Physiology. The latter was a clinician and experimentalist. He differentiated between cerebrum and cerebellum, noted the greater complexity of convolutions in man as contrasted with animals, and related this anatomical feature to greater intelligence (4). In a Royal patient with melancholia, he noted increased pulse rate that appeared to be indicative of an unacknowledged love interest (15). This theme of the love-sick patient has recurred in remarkably similar descriptions through the years and has been found in an account about Galen. It was ascribed many years later, in the seventeenth century, to a clinical experience of Jacques Ferrand who was to write *De la Maladie d'Amour, ou Mélancholie Erotique* (1623). The story has been described as having acquired a legendary quality in the history of psychiatry (Schneck, 15). The clinical experience of Erasistratus has been represented pictorially and may be found with other scenes and portraits of psychiatric significance in Bettmann's historical volume (16).

Asclepiades of Bithynia, who settled in Rome about 91 B. C., followed Erasistratus in rejecting the humoral theory of disease promulgated by Hippocrates, and adhered instead to the atomic concepts of Democritus (4). He was interested in psychiatric patients and Major regards him as a pioneer in humane treatment. Light and well ventilated rooms were prescribed with occupational therapy, procedures for increasing attention span and improving memory, and music therapy for calming patients. He was interested in the characteristics of mental disease in general, and of the psychological reactions shown in illness accompanied by fever with lethargy or excitement and delerious conditions (3). It has been pointed out that Asclepiades had a fashionable practice and had long been regarded as virtually a charlatan although this opinion has since been revised (4). He was a psychologically perceptive man who was attentive to the patient as an individual. Asclepiades was in medical practice during the period when Greek medicine was assuming its role of importance in Rome (5). As for his place in the listings of fathers to the various specialties, we find that Major is willing to view him as the Father of Geriatrics, and Lewis says he has been referred to as the Father of Psychiatry. Lewis also notes his opposition to mechanical restraints, an issue which was to be highly significant later on in the history of psychiatry. Asclepiades is also credited with the differentiation between hallucinations, delusions, and illusions (5).

The famous *De Re Medicina* was written by Celsus, a Roman scholar who was not a physician. He was a man of encyclopedic knowledge. At the onset of the Christian era, Celsus included, in his writings, material on nervous and mental disease. Among his descriptions was mental derangement which could be chronic, without danger to life, and characterized in part by impaired judgment or false images. Lewis believes that the observations may relate to schizophrenia and paranoia (5). He noted a variety of mental ailments previously described by others. As descriptions are traced through the years from one writer to another it seems that diagnostic labels varied at times and overlapped too. This has been so, of course, in more recent years as well. *De Re Medicina* was written in Latin and has been rated one of the great medical classics (4).

A significant clinician of the Roman Empire was Aretaeus who has been said by some to have lived and practiced in the first century A. D. (3), and by others in the second (4). He described epileptic aurae and was able to distinguish between involutional and senile psychoses. Lewis is of the opinion that Aretaeus antedated Kraepelin by 1800 years in his views of the manic-depressive cycle (5). He was inclined to believe that manic states were more common in the younger and melancholic states in the older age group. Worthy of note is his attention to the personalities of people prior to development of their mental illnesses, and regarding the latter he was observant of ideational content. Zilboorg judges his interests as an early evaluation of some mental illnesses as psychological extensions of normal personality patterns (3). What has been said of Celsus in connection with schizophrenia and paranoia may be said also of Aretaeus. Additionally, he saw mania as an intermittent occurrence that was curable, in contrast with his dim view of senile reactions. In line with this, he was regarded highly for his prognostic abilities. While advancing on these fronts, he retained the conventional impression of hysteria and its alleged relation to the wandering uterus. According to Mettler (17), Aretaeus' treatment of phrenitis suggests that it was a symptomatic febrile delerium which may have included meningitis.

It is clear that through these years medical interest in varieties of psychological reactions was present to greater or lesser degree, with gradual increase in knowledge and growing awareness of the complexities in psychiatric illness. For example, in the case of ever present melancholia, Rufus of Ephesus (c. 100 A. D.) noted the admixture of obsessional patterns with depression, and the delusional attributes in the involutional reactions (5). Among his many clinical and anatomical observations is his discovery of the optic chiasm and discernment of functional attributes of the nervous system. Of special interest to psychiatrists is his work, *On the Interrogation of the Patient.* Here is stress on the importance of taking a patient's history with careful questioning of the patient and people known to him (4). Characteristics of the patient and his way of life are inquired into, and an effort is made to see him in more total perspective. We get the impression of the development of an approach to the patient suggestive of more recent fulfillments associated with psychobiological concepts.

As for trends, the issue of mechanical restraints and opposition to their unwarranted use has been referred to in connection with Asclepiades. Again, such thinking appears when we consider Soranus and his contributions early in the second century A. D. He is famous, of course, in the history of gynecology. At least one historian is so impressed with his humanitarianism and psychological sensitivities, as to consider him almost in the ranks of the great reformers to follow, Chiarugi, Pinel, and Tuke (3). He was sparing in his use of drugs, and generally soothing in his ministrations with employment of occupational therapy techniques for the mentally ill.

Caelius Aurelianus was a Latin translator of Soranus, some of whose writings survived under his name (2). Living in the fourth or fifth century, Caelius Aurelianus has been rated the greatest physician to follow soon after Galen. Among his activities was considerable attentiveness to the mentally ill, concern with their comfort, and censure of chains or flogging (4). Use of physical restraint was minimal and careful. Theatrical entertainment, reading, and exercise played a part in treatment. Excessive drug therapy was criticized (5). A point of interest, in contrast to otherwise enlightened views, was the acceptance by this physician of the belief in demons, under the guise of men, seducing women sexually. This belief was to play an increasingly important role in psychopathology during the next few centuries. In medieval psychiatry its powerful influence was especially highlighted.

The man who was to influence the field of medicine long after his death, lived and worked during the second century. Galen (130-200), as Boring has declared, assumed for medicine the authoritative role paralleled by Aristotle's influence in philosophy and science (18). It is of interest that Galen's biographer, Sarton, the historian of science, declared that at times he received a share of fame greater than he deserved although his actual greatness can be assessed now in better perspective (19). He was verbose, aggressive and vain, yet an excellent anatomist and physiologist. As an anatomist, his learning was derived largely from dissection of animals. Ackerknecht sees him as the greatest medical experimentalist up to the seventeenth century (2). Some of his written works were lost and others have been found in Arabic translations (20). Whereas Major has referred to Galen as skilled in psychosomatic medicine (4), Lewis is not impressed with his contributions to psychotherapy and notes that he was essentially limited to physical and drug therapies of his time (21). He was famed for his eclecticism and was a renowned teleologist (3).

Zilboorg indicates that an important view propagated by Galen and mentioned previously by Aretaeus was that symptoms are not always an expression of disease in the body parts which reflect them. Another part may actually be diseased and symptoms may appear in an area somewhat removed from it, by consensus. Mania and melancholia were considered manifestations of brain disease, but alcoholic intoxication was viewed as a mental disease by consensus only. Galen saw the brain as the center of all sensation and motion. Dementia and imbecility were based on alterations in animal spirits and coldness and humidity of the brain (3). He rejected the idea of the wandering uterus in connection with hysteria, and varying descriptions of his opinions as to etiology have been offered. They seem to relate to some notion of uterine congestion (3, 5). Lewis interprets his view as retention of "ovarian products" in the female, with too many or too few sexual relationships with men. Lewis also ascribes to Galen the origin of the analogy between man as microcosm and the universe as macrocosm, a feature of medieval medicine that was to become important in the thinking of Paracelsus.

REFERENCES

1. Drabkin, I. E.: Remarks on Ancient Psychopathology. *Isis, 46*:223, 1955.
2. Ackerknecht, E. H.: *A Short History of Medicine.* New York, Ronald Press, 1955.
3. Zilboorg, G. and Henry, G. W.: *A History of Medical Psychology.* New York, W. W. Norton, 1941.
4. Major, R. H.: *A History of Medicine.* Springfield, Thomas, 1954.
5. Lewis, N. D. C.: *A Short History of Psychiatric Achievement.* London, Chapman and Hall, 1942.
6. Tourney, G.: Empedocles and Freud, Heraclitus and Jung. *Bull. Hist. Med., 30*:109, 1956.
7. Roddis, L. H.: The Life and Influence of Hippocrates. *Curr. Med. Dig., 23*:26, 1956.
8. Hippocrates: The Oath (Trans. by Francis Adams) in *The Greek Classics,* Vol. 6, ed. by M. M. Miller. New York, Vincent Parke, 1909.
9. Veith, I.: Medical Ethics Throughout the Ages. *A. M. A. Arch. Int. Med. 100*:504, 1957.
10. Wall, J. H.: The Changing Concepts of Involutional Melancholia. *J. South Carolina Med. Assn., 53*:383, 1957.
11. Menninger, K., Ellenberger, H., Pruyser, P., and Mayman, M.: The Unitary Concept of Mental Illness. *Bull. Menninger Clin., 22*:4, 1958.
12. Block, S. L.: Hippocrates on Psychotherapy by the General Practitioner. *New Eng. J. Med., 256*:559, 1957.
13. Murphy, G.: *Historical Introduction to Modern Psychology.* New York, Harcourt, Brace, 1949.
14. Singer, C.: *A Short History of Medicine.* New York, Oxford University Press, 1928.
15. Schneck, J. M.: The Love-Sick Patient in the History of Medicine. *J. Hist. Med. & Allied Sc., 12*:266, 1957.
16. Bettmann, O. L.: *A Pictorial History of Medicine.* Springfield,

Thomas, 1956.

17. Mettler, F. A.: In Mettler, C. C.: *History of Medicine*. Philadelphia, Blakiston, 1947.
18. Boring, E. G.: *A History of Experimental Psychology*. New York, Appleton-Century-Crofts, 1950.
19. Sarton, G.: *Galen of Pergamon*. Lawrence, Kansas, University of Kansas Press, 1954.
20. Bender, G. A.: *A History of Medicine In Pictures*. Therap. Notes 65 (No. 3), 1958.
21. Lewis, N. D. C.: Historical Roots of Psychotherapy. *Am. J. Psychiat., 114*:795, 1958.
22. Ackerknecht, E. H.: *Rudolf Virchow, Doctor, Statesman, Anthropologist*. Madison, Wis., University of Wisconsin, 1953.

Chapter 3

THE MIDDLE AGES

The transition from the Greek and Roman period to the Middle Ages was gradual. Later, the demarcation between Middle Ages and Renaissance was to be fluid too. Empiricism in medicine suffered a decline during this period. There was growth of theological and metaphysical influence (1). The field of medicine concerned with mental illness gradually was taken over by the priest. More and more as the years passed, demonology took hold. Its influence was powerful and frightful. The supernaturalism of primitive and archaic medicine was followed by the naturalism of the Hippocratic era. In time this gave way to the revival of supernaturalism, the spread of demonology, and the extension of faith-healing under the dominance of theology. Zilboorg has described this change by saying that the field of mental disease was torn from medicine and that medical psychology practically disappeared. Bromberg has seen this period as one wherein faith-healing was organized and exploited by the Church of Rome and became the outstanding feature of mental healing in the Occidental world until the growth of psychological science in the eighteenth century (2). The medieval period incorporated the devastating destruction of the Black Death in 1348 (3), the possession of the masochistic flagellants, the dancing manias, and the advance of the witchcraft cult.

There was much darkness but also some light. In the fourth century, general hospitals were established and a few possessed separate sections for the mentally ill. According to Lewis, a hospital specifically for patients with mental disease appeared in Jerusalem during the year 490 (4). With the rise of Arabian medicine, the teachings of Galen and Hippocrates were spread further, yet there was little advance in the treatment of psychiatric disorder.

It has been affirmed, however, that the clinical observations of the Arabs were not colored by the demonological blanket that clouded the Christian world (1).

Rhazes (c. 841-926) was a great Persian physician who wrote in Arabic. He was influenced by Hippocrates and Galen and his clinical descriptions were impressive (5). As was true of some of the hospitals referred to previously, the one headed by Rhazes in Baghdad, a large institution, had a section for the mentally ill. Descriptions of many forms of psychiatric illness were prepared by a writer, Najab, who was perhaps a contemporary of Rhazes (1). Treatment procedure differed little from methods used and described before.

Rhazes began his studies in medicine when he was forty, but Avicenna (980-1037) is said to have established a reputation in medicine when only eighteen (5). He was a man of remarkable intellect. Whereas his *Canon* retained popularity for many years after publication, Lewis was impressed by its inconsistencies and superstitions (4). Avicenna was influenced by Aristotle. His medical psychology has been called eclectic (1). He placed memory function in the posterior region of the brain, imagination in the anterior, and regarded the latter as the source of hallucinations. The ventricles controlled the major functions of the brain. One particular statement of Avicenna has been singled out for mention by Lewis. This was to the effect that one disease could be the means of curing another, such as quartan malaria used for epilepsy. He did not subscribe to the role of demonological influence in melancholia (1). His dominating medical stature persisted for many centuries (9).

Avenzoar (1094-1162), a practical physician, was not highly impressed by Avicenna's work. His own reputation was such that the medical historian, Garrison, has called him the greatest clinician of the Western Caliphate (6). He is credited with having objected to the use of the cautery in mental illness for which it may have become an accepted therapeutic device (1). It appears to be the first such reference (4).

Maimonides (1135-1208) was born in Cordoba (5). He was the foremost Jewish philosopher of his time and is regarded as a universal scholar (7). He emphasized principles of medical practice and has been compared in some ways to Sir William Osler (8). He has also been designated the first medieval author to emphasize psychological elements in theory and practice. Although this point is made in comparison to what has been called the crude psychotherapy in the descriptions of clinical cases by Rhazes and Avicenna, it is necessary to be wary of overemphasizing his importance in this respect. In any case he did take emotional factors into consideration and this pertained to all forms of illness (7).

With continuing development of Arabian medicine, hospitals, libraries, and institutions of learning were established. Contributions to psychiatry may not have been especially outstanding, but treatment of the mentally ill was more humane than it had often been before. Lewis (4) feels this may have been based on the view of such patients as divinely inspired. During this period, Johannes Actuarius (1250-1300) was interested in fantasy and memory, perception and judgment. His therapeutic regime in mental illness stressed hygiene, and music was prescribed for stimulation of the intellect. Purgatives and narcotics continued to play a role also in treatment (4).

Clerics gradually assumed an increasingly important role in medical writing and practice, and essentially clinical data on mental illness began to dwindle. Psychiatric concerns moved into the domain of those who searched for heretics and psychological issues fused with, and became confused with theological problems. Eventually it seemed that what Zilboorg has called a period of contrasts set in. Hospitals and establishments of higher learning were developed, and the Inquisition took root (1).

Bartholomaeus, teaching and writing during the thirteenth century (5), was clinical in his approach to illness with a humane attitude toward the mentally ill and an interest in occupational activity for such patients. He has, however, been considered advanced for his time (1). For impairment in sexual functioning and deterioration of intellectual faculties it was the witches who were sought as causative agents. At the same time some therapies in vogue included mercury for impotence, gold and silver for melancholia. And it has been suggested that increasing faith in miracles with a monotony in the culture of this medieval period probably fostered the growth of mental illness which tended to engender more fear than pity (1). The severely ill were often turned out of their homes and left to wander off and to fend for themselves. This in turn probably promoted further anxiety among the populace and encouraged spread of superstition.

Of those branded witches, many were undoubtedly mentally ill. Bromberg (2) remarks of the heretical witch that the acting out of rebelliousness through hysterical mechanisms seems to have been involved, and the psychopathology of witches is revealed clearly in records of the time. Witchcraft in its mass delusion has been seen as a perversion of faith which, instead of serving as a meaningful psychological support, became a foundation for intolerance. Possibilities for growth of a helpful, significant psychotherapy were dampened by the frightening cult. For those who whipped it into a frenzy, the symptoms of neuroses and psychoses were not indications of sickness. They were manifestations of a Satanic agency.

Even as the Renaissance approached with awakening of intellectual interests and pursuits, the impact of demonology became more pronounced. Mass psychopathology in the form of the aforementioned masochistic flagellant and similar groups spread over many parts of Europe. An abnormal religiosity took hold and absorbed much of medical psychology. This became part of what has been called a codified demonology, and legal processes replaced treatment efforts for the mentally sick (1). Yet, in some places there were evidences of a healthy psychiatric tradition, and on the basis of events in these areas comes the declaration at times that Spain was the cradle of psychiatry (10). Historians such as Morejon and Ullersperger have been impressed by the role of Spain in the development of humane psychiatric hospitals and treatment during this period, and it seems that the renowned reformer, Pinel, looked to Spain rather than to England or Germany for such good example. Whether or not he exaggerated the merits of the Zaragoza asylum as has been claimed, he felt it deserved attention in promoting the welfare of the mentally ill and mentioned it in his *Traité Médico — Philosophique Sur L'Aliénation Mentale*

(1809). This asylum was established in 1425. Of course, as far as removal of chains is concerned, the role of Caelius Aurelianus, for example, has already been mentioned. Prior to Zaragoza, in Spain itself, elimination of unnecessary restraint and employment of moral treatment found its way into the practice of physicians in Valencia in 1409. Exercises, recreational and occupational therapy, and attention to general hygiene and a dietary regime were under supervision of the hospital doctors. Later, a hospital at Sevilla was founded in 1436, and the mentally ill obtained another haven. More were to appear about this time, followed by the Toledo Hospital de Inocentes in 1480 and the mental hospital established in 1527 in Granada by Ferdinand and Isabella. All of these good efforts were to deteriorate soon. According to Bassoe (10) this coincided with the northern invasion of the orthodox Christian overwhelming the southern and eastern influence of the Mohammedan culture. The same author sees Greece as the mother of psychiatry, and while Spain was the cradle, psychiatry became neglected and the Moors grew more fanatic and intolerant. As a result it is doubted that the beneficial work, as outlined, made a significant impression on other areas of Europe. It was lost with the intellectual isolation of Spain, and is believed to have been known to few until Pinel visited this region in the Napoleonic era (10).

REFERENCES

1. Zilboorg, G. and Henry, G. W.: *A History of Medical Psychology.* New York, W. W. Norton, 1941.
2. Bromberg, W.: *Man Above Humanity.* Philadelphia, J. B. Lippincott, 1954.
3. Ackerknecht, E. H.: *A Short History of Medicine.* New York, Ronald Press, 1955.
4. Lewis, N. D. C.: *A Short History of Psychiatric Achievement.* London, Chapman and Hall, 1942.
5. Major, R. H.: *A History of Medicine.* Springfield, Thomas, 1954.
6. Garrison, F. H.: *Introduction to the History of Medicine.* Philadelphia, Saunders, 1929.
7. Leibowitz, J. O.: Maimonides on Medical Practice. *Bull. Hist.*

Med., *31*:309, 1957.

8. Macht, D.: Moses Maimonides, Physician and Scientist. *Bull. Hist. Med.*, *3*:585, 1935.
9. Robinson, V.: *The Story of Medicine.* New York, Albert and Charles Boni, 1931.
10. Bassoe, P.: Spain as the Cradle of Psychiatry. *Am. J. Psychiat.*, *101*:731, 1945.

Courtesy of the New York Academy of Medicine

Chapter 4

THE RENAISSANCE

In the beginnings of the Renaissance and during the course of its development with artistic and scientific creativity, witchcraft continued not only to exist but was flamed to new heights. Between 1487 and 1489 there was published the *Malleus Maleficarum* (1). The *Witch Hammer,* an inquisitorial textbook (2), was authored by the notorious theologians, Johann Sprenger and Heinrich Kraemer. Described by Zilboorg as methodical and persistent Germans, they were men with a mission, and the mission was the extermination of witches. Demonology had a misogynic coloring (3) and men of learning were not exempt from this popular delusion.

With political, religious, and scientific support too, Sprenger and Kraemer went about their work. Authority of Pope Innocent VIII was obtained in 1484 (1), and they set out in their book to prove the existence of witches and witchcraft, to describe methods of identifying witches, and to illustrate ways to examine and sentence them. The reaction was catastrophic, and among the victims of this plague were thousands of mentally ill. One judge in particular is said to have pronounced the death penalty by burning for eight hundred women during a period of sixteen years (3). This widespread pathological phenomenon has been related to the unsettled state of the times, with instability of the powers in control during the medieval period, and the restructuring of social forces lending itself to the creation of anxiety and turmoil. The witch-hunt sounded pious and it could be used as a rationalization for the destruction of whatever one wished to oppose. These points have been clearly delineated (1). It has been shown also that accounts of this demonology demonstrated the widespread existence of mental illness with records of its manifestations. Of course, what was discerned could only be misused by the misguided. Fortunately the acceptance of demonological beliefs did not prevent men of healing from exerting useful efforts in humanitarian works. Notable examples such as the distinguished surgeon, Ambroise Paré (1510-1590), stand out in bold relief (4).

Not long after the *Witch Hammer* was published, Juan Luis Vives was born in Valencia during the year 1492. He has been called the Father of Modern Psychology (5). He was reared in a religious setting, and as a young man he went to Paris for additional study. Later he spent much time in Bruges and Louvain as well as five years in England (1). Contrary to what may be gleaned from attitudes of the time, Vives made a point of the intellectual and cultural significance of women in civilization (1). His outlook was distinctly humanitarian and he had an interest in public welfare, the common people, and the plight of the poor. This humane feeling naturally carried over to his interest in the mentally ill as people first of all. His emphasis was on gentleness, and the use of restraint was to be selective, judicious, and with calming intent.

Zilboorg has evaluated Vives in detail (1). He discounted the role of planetary influence on mental functioning. In a modern vein he sensed the importance of psychological associations, delineating their evidence through "similarity, contiguity, and opposites." He has been credited with being the first in the history of psychology to fathom the emotional issues underlying some associations, and the retrieving of long-forgotten experiences through processes of association. The importance of this aspect of memory has prompted the claim that Vives' knowledge of memory functioning significantly antedated the contributions of Hartley and Hobbes. Not only has Zilboorg asserted that the importance of Vives has not as yet been sufficiently understood, but it has also been claimed that he achieved understandings exceeding those of his predecessors. Accepting him as the Father of Modern Empirical Psychology, Zilboorg rates Vives as a forerunner of twentieth century dynamic psychology (1). Despite these claims, Bassoe has seen him as a seclusive philosopher and doubts that he could have had direct impact during his lifetime on the care of the mentally ill in Spain (5). Vives died in 1540.

Of quite different temperament was Vives' contemporary, Paracelsus (Phillippus Aureolus Theophrastus Bombastus von Hohenheim, 1493-1541). Much has been written about him, and at times he is regarded as one of the three great medical figures of the Renaissance, the other two, as Haggard declares, being Paré and Vesalius (6). In many ways he was coarse, gross, and impatient. He wrote and lectured in the vernacular. His thinking was not demonological. Heat and cold were important in mental illness, according to Paracelsus. Heat was involved in some maniacal states, so scarification of fingers and toes might be helpful in letting air enter in order to diminish excess heat (1). Again the issue of precursors of Freud is introduced when Zilboorg declares that *chorea lasciva* suggested the sexual elements in hysteria, a point to be elucidated in psychoanalytic studies long afterwards. The same historian credits Paracelsus with having made the first reference in the history of medical psychology to unconscious motivation in neurotic illness.

For Paracelsus, mental illness was a natural disability, and spiritual in the sense of unhealthy alteration in the *spiritus vitae*. Understandings of disease were significant, but treatment was of prime importance and this healer was a man of action (1).

Major (7) regards *Diseases That Deprive Man of His Reason* as an early classic on mental disease. Pachter (8), Paracelsus' biographer, sees this book written in 1528 to be dominated by chemical ideas. It is well known, of course, that chemical concerns played a very strong role in many of his views and teachings. Pachter has also expressed the opinion that Paracelsus separated spiritual from physical diseases, but that his notion of spirit was materialistic. *Spiritus vitae* had no relation to soul or reason, and this biographer believes that his subject conceived of all diseases as somatic rather than psychological. It would seem, then, that Pachter does not adopt a holistic view of illness, judging by the description, and he does not ascribe a holistic concept to Paracelsus. The attempt to approach the subject historically appears to become confused further when he writes that Paracelsus treated all diseases as "somatic or psychosomatic rather than psychological disorders."

In addition to St. Vitus' dance, Paracelsus described epilepsy, mania, hysteria, and other forms of psychological illness (8). He observed a connection between endemic goiter and cretinism. He followed the concept of signatures in drug prescription, with its correlation between the appearance of the plant origin and the organ on which the drug was presumed to act (7).

Paracelsus was a rebel and is said to have encouraged his students to prepare a special bonfire for burning the classics. Garrison repeats this story (9). He stressed the importance of investigation, and the book burning occurred when he became a professor at Basel. He was Swiss by birth, but led a life of travel. Among the older authorities he decried were Galen, Hippocrates, and Avicenna. Attitudes toward Paracelsus have varied, and in her study of the development of medical bibliography, Brodman has pointed out that his contributions to medicine have been evaluated differently on many occasions (10).

It is believed that one of the origins of animal magnetism, as elaborated by Mesmer in the eighteenth century, lay in a concept of body magnetism favored by Paracelsus (11). To some extent there is a parallel between these two physicians in relation to Brodman's comment about differing assessments being made at different time periods.

There is to be found an independent spirit too in Heinrich Cornelius Agrippa of Nettesheim (1486-1535), an older contemporary of Paracelsus. Advocating humane treatment for the mentally ill, iron collars and chains were considered by him so often unnecessary, and it was his belief that if indicated a padded cell would be more efficacious for protection of the patient and others (12).

Cornelius Agrippa held doctorates in medicine, law, and theology. He was a pioneer in the strong opposition to demonological philosophy (1). Although he is not considered an original thinker, he was bold in action, and learned. Like Paracelsus he seemed to be at opposite poles with the medical profession of his day. He was held suspect, was disliked, and died poverty-stricken and alone (1). A friend of those oppressed by the inquisition, he had a powerful enemy in one of its leaders, Nicolas Savin, when serving as advocate in the city of Metz (3). In time, Agrippa had to flee amidst slanderous condemnation, and he was accused of associating with the devil. He was the author of *On the Uncertainty and Vanity of all Sciences,* a criticism of witchcraft and magic. Three years before he died, Agrippa had Johann Weyer (1515-1588) as a student. It is Weyer whom Zilboorg regards as having made the greatest contribution to psychiatry during the Renaissance (1).

While artists of the sixteenth century were portraying traveling quacks, depicting the stone cutters removing their objects from the body, and in the case of insanity, enucleating stones from the head (13), Weyer was pursuing his methodical, serious studies. Whereas some have conceded Weyer's place as the "true founder" of modern psychiatry (14), others have freely acknowledged his credulities. A curious item, for example, is Weyer's decision about the actual number of demons. There were, he said, seven million, four hundred nine thousand, one hundred and twenty seven, and all of them were controlled by seventy-nine princes (15). Despite such oddities, not unusual in themselves at that time, Weyer has been described as a simple man, yet a rebel. He is one of the relatively few, perhaps, in the history of medicine (16).

Aside from Weyer's brave and open statement that alleged witches were often mentally ill and not the devil's associates, he is also credited with being a capable clinician. In support of this is his account of scurvey, and female sex organ malformation (2).

Weyer studied medicine in Paris after his contact with Cornelius Agrippa. He was a pious, sensitive, and quiet man (1). By birth he is considered by some a Netherlander, and by others a Rhenish German. In medicine he was a good practitioner and original observer. Aside from his gynecological interests mentioned above and including the invention of a vaginal speculum, he described quartan fever and the "English Sweat." But mental disease was a predominant interest. He attempted to distinguish malefactors with criminal intent or behavior from the mentally ill regarded as witches. His views are presented in *De Praestigiis Daemonum* (1563). Weyer was interested in the emotional life of his patients and was curious about ideation under the influence of drugs. He accumulated a wealth of personal clinical experience and his accounts of mental illness permit comparisons with current findings, pointing up the obvious identities in the varieties of existent mental derangement. Although he did not issue a textbook dealing with psychiatric illness, Zilboorg has stressed that the richness of his experience serves as a base for a descriptive psychopathology (1). Weyer was a keen observer of personality functioning and was interested in understanding pathology without succumbing to immediate reactions of shock and condemnation. In his evaluation of what he regarded as abnormal fantasies, he inferred some type of pathological process within the individual himself.

Weyer's contributions have been outlined to indicate that he was the first physician with a major interest in mental illness, thus foreshadowing the development of psychiatry as a medical specialty. He was the first clinical and descriptive psychiatrist to presage the later descriptive system of psychiatry developed toward the close of the nineteenth century. He was interested in a variety of aspects of psychopathology although he supplied no specific theory of his own. His role was important in the gradual separation of medical psychology from theology. Weyer came into conflict with lawyers and legal processes because of his views, and Zilboorg wishes also to regard him as the first true medico-legal psychiatrist (1). While all of this transpired, the influence of the *Malleus Maleficarum* was continuing. It has been acknowledged that Weyer's immediate influence was not great. In line with this, as has already been pointed out (Schneck, 17), Sir William Osler regarded Reginald Scot (to be mentioned later) and Johannes Wierus (Johann Weyer) as "really anomalies" because their views differed so significantly from those of their contemporaries (18).

While not denying the devil, Weyer refused to take his alleged manifestations at face value. And, as indicated, he was a careful clinician rather than a reformer like Scot (3). In any case, this did not prevent him from encountering enemies, one of the most powerful of whom was Jean Bodin (1530-1596), a man with legal training and vast knowledge. He attacked Weyer's views directly, and after Bodin these attacks in substance were to continue for many decades. A significant claim was that "what may prove not true in nature may still be true in the law." This view has had great impact on medico-legal relationships, and in the field of psychiatry it manifests itself in discrepancies between "medical insanity" and "legal insanity" (1). After Bodin, the physician Paul Zacchias (1584-1659), who pioneered in legal medicine, actually was closer to Bodin's views than to Weyer's.

While traditional demonological views retained their hold, and the birth of an interest in the individual was slowly making its way, the ideas of Weyer were reenforced in the efforts of Reginald Scot, a layman. He attacked the belief in witchcraft and published his *Discoverie of Witchcraft* in 1584. In the behavior of self-confessed "witches" he looked for naturalistic explanations. He was concerned about legal injustice in their trials (3). His publication was ordered burned by King James.

Belief in the devil and his influence did not necessarily prevent the performance of good works. This is illustrated further in the case of Felix Plater (1536-1614) who made personal contact with the mentally ill and the mentally deficient in the dungeons to which they were confined. Plater is regarded as one of the earliest classifiers of disease (2). In his efforts to evaluate mental disease, he attempted to distinguish between acquired, congenital, and hereditary afflictions (19). He described obsessions, and Lewis (11) rates as excellent his accounts of states of stupor. Indications of *flexibilitas cerea* are recorded. This term, however, was not in use at that time. While he thought of the brain as affected in these disorders, his observations of extreme or bizarre derangement with delusional and hallucinatory attributes prompted him to consider them reflections of possession by the devil (1).

Consistent with Plater's interest in the brain is the recent claim that he supplied, apparently, the first account of a meningioma. This Swiss physician's report is considered an excellent clinical and anatomic description. The work appeared in 1614 and the title reads, *Observationum in hominis affectibus plerisque, corpori et animo, functionum laesione, dolore, aliave molestia et vitio incommodantibus, libri tres* (20).

Attention to the brain as the source of various forms of illness can also be found among others. An example is Charles Lepois (1563-1633) whose concern with hysteria turned him away from the uterus and to the brain, with the claim made, as at times before and after him, that men as well as women were subject to the illness.

During the sixteenth century two orientations in medical psychology can be discerned (1). In one, the activities of the human mind are linked to the human body for attempts at understanding. The concept of the soul is bypassed for this purpose. The emphasis is psychological, empirical, descriptive, and experimental. Francis Bacon (1561-1626) is allied to this view because of emphasis on a measurable, physiological psychology. Then, as Zilboorg has put it, the second orientation moves into the area of psychological motivation with concern over individual and social behavior. What man does and thinks and feels becomes important. This involves a degree of scientific detachment by the observer and a type of maturity which was approached when Freud devised his early views. This theme takes us back to Juan Luis Vives. Consistent with this outline is the claim that Vives was "the first true forerunner of Freud" (1). The orientations and trends summarized now must be seen as having been far more complex and groping than this overall account would appear to indicate. We must be willing to acknowledge that the developmental path of psychiatric growth consisted of rocky terrain, serious obstacles as well as occasional smooth areas, and numerous misleading side roads with dead ends.

While Francis Bacon was pursuing his formulation of scientific method (he has been referred to as the father of the empirical scientific method), and in the midst of his work on the inductive law of scientific discovery (11), what was happening in the area of hospital growth and patient care? In 1547 the monastery of St. Mary of Bethlehem of London became a mental hospital. "Bedlam" became a popular word. At quite a distance from it, San Hipolito in Mexico, 1566, served as the first hospital in the Americas for the care of the mentally ill (11). It is believed that this institution was not limited at first to psychiatric patients but that it was necessary to place such limits later because of numerous admissions of the mentally ill. And we find additionally that Lisbon, Portugal is said to have been the home of religious institutes for the care of mental patients since 1539. Joâo de Deus is specifically designated as having considered the mentally ill, in the sixteenth century, as afflicted with sickness calling for humane care and treatment (21). Then, as the century came to a close, the word *psychologia* appeared. Rudolf Goeckel published in 1590, *Psychology, or the Improvement of Man.* Four years later his pupil, Otto Casmann, issued *Psychologia Anthropologica* (1).

REFERENCES

1. Zilboorg, G. and Henry, G. W.: *A History of Medical Psychology.* New York, W. W. Norton, 1941.
2. Ackerknecht, E. H.: *A Short History of Medicine.* New York, Ronald Press, 1955.
3. Bromberg, W.: *Man Above Humanity.* Philadelphia, J. B. Lippincott, 1954.
4. Sigerist, H. E.: *The Great Doctors.* New York, W. W. Norton, 1933.
5. Bassoe, P.: Spain as the Cradle of Psychiatry. *Am. J. Psychiat., 101*:731, 1945.
6. Haggard, H. W.: *Mystery, Magic, and Medicine.* New York, Doubleday, Doran & Co., 1933.
7. Major, R. H.: *A History of Medicine.* Springfield, Thomas, 1954.
8. Pachter, H. M.: *Paracelsus, Magic Into Science.* New York, Henry Schuman, 1951.
9. Garrison, F. H.: *Introduction to the History of Medicine.* Philadelphia, Saunders, 1929.
10. Brodman, E.: *The Development of Medical Bibliography.* Baltimore, Medical Library Association, 1954.
11. Lewis, N. D. C.: *A Short History of Psychiatric Achievement.* London, Chapman and Hall, 1942.
12. Atkinson, D. T.: *Magic, Myth and Medicine.* New York, World Publishing Company, 1956.
13. Fry, C. C.: The Sixteenth Century Cures for Lunacy. *Am. J. Psychiat., 103*:351, 1946.
14. Leigh, D.: Recurrent Themes in the History of Psychiatry. *Med. Hist., 1*:237, 1957.
15. Norman, H. J.: Progress in the Treatment of Mental Disorders. *Med. Bookman and Historian, 2*:161, 1948.
16. Zilboorg, G.: Psychology and Medical History. In Galdston, I.:

On the Utility of Medical History. New York, International Universities Press, 1957.

17. Schneck, J. M.: Sir Thomas Browne, Religio Medici, and the History of Psychiatry. *Am. J. Psychiat., 114*:657, 1958.
18. Osler, W.: *Selected Writings of Sir William Osler.* London, Oxford University Press, 1951.
19. Menninger, W. C.: *Fundamentals of Psychiatry.* Topeka, Capper, 1943.
20. Netsky, G. and Lapresle, J.: The First Account of a Meningioma. *Bull. Hist. Med., 30*:465,1956.
21. De Barahona Fernandes, H. J.: Contemporary Psychiatry in Portugal. *Am. J. Psychiat., 114*:923, 1958.

Chapter 5

THE SEVENTEENTH CENTURY

"It is useless to argue that any result of witchcraft may be a fantasy and unreal, because such a fantasy cannot be procured without resort to the power of the devil, and it is necessary that there should be made a contract with the devil, by which contract the witch truly and actually binds herself to be the servant of the devil and devotes herself to the devil, and this is not done in any dream or under any illusion, but she herself bodily and truly cooperates with, and conjoins herself to, the devil. For this indeed is the end of all witchcraft; whether it be the casting of spells by a look or by a formula of words or by some other charm, it is all of the devil.

"This then is our proposition: devils by their art do bring about evil effects through witchcraft, yet it is true that without the assistance of some agent they cannot make any form, either substantial or accidental, and we do not maintain that they can inflict damage without the assistance of some agent, but with such an agent diseases, and any other human passions or ailments, can be brought about, and these are real and true. . . .

"As for the first question, why a greater number of witches is found in the fragile female sex than among men; it is indeed a fact that it were idle to contradict, since it is accredited by actual experience, apart from the verbal testimony of credible witnesses. . . .

"Now the wickedness of women is spoken of in Ecclesiasticus XXV: There is no head above the head of a serpent: and there is no wrath above the wrath of a woman. I had rather dwell with a lion and a dragon than to keep house with a wicked woman. . . .

"To conclude. All witchcraft comes from carnal lust, which is in women insatiable. There are three things that are never satisfied, yea, a fourth thing which says not, it is enough; that is the mouth of the womb. Wherefore for the sake of fulfilling their lusts they consort even with devils. More such reasons could be brought forward, but to the understanding it is sufficiently clear that it is no matter for wonder that there are more women than men found infected with the heresy of witchcraft."

These allegations are from the *Witch Hammer,* and parts were deservedly included by Ehrenwald in his anthology of writings significant in the development of psychiatric thought (1). The opening words of the previous chapter on the Renaissance dealt also with Sprenger and Kraemer's *Malleus Maleficarum.* This emphasis is reinforced now because the witchcraft influence continued through the seventeenth century, into the eighteenth, and to a decreasing extent even afterwards. Occasionally today we read news items about witchcraft cults and accusations, items which are echoes from the distant past. Based as they are on psychopathology of the accused or the accusor, these occurrences continue to be of psychiatric interest. During the seventeenth century in particular, belief in the devil and involvement in issues dealing with witchcraft were linked with men bearing considerable reputations in medicine and general scientific areas. As for its presence today, we find the following: "The West German state of Lower Saxony is a place where 1,200 Volkswagens materialize daily in one of the world's most modern factories. It is also a place where the belief in and practice of witchcraft is so widespread that the Ministry of Social Affairs, having put in a year investigating the phenomenon, has now launched an educational campaign to exorcise superstition and purge Saxon minds of their fantasies. But the Ministry is resigned to something less than overnight results in communities where new ideas, like strangers, are coolly received" (2). And as for its persistence in earlier years, we shall trace evidences of it again during the course of medico-psychological growth.

One representative of seventeenth century medicine is Thomas Willis (1621-1675). Ackerknecht designates his orientation as that of an iatrochemist (3). His name remains associated with the circle of Willis. He was aware of the sweetness of urine in diabetics and he left descriptions of typhoid fever, puerperal fever and myasthenia gravis. Also, he has been credited with an early account of general paresis. Willis was a follower of Sylvius (Franz de le Boë), the Leyden clinician considered a leader of the physicians who worked much with chemical ideas, thus giving rise to the iatrochemist designation (4).

Lewis considers the description of general paresis to have been actually the first definite clinical account of this condition (5). Willis was impressed with the role of the brain in mental activity and, as we have seen, this actually is the continuation of a point of view which moved to the forefront repeatedly over the centuries and was to be reenforced again at later dates. He regarded the cerebellum as the seat of vital activity and believed that different areas of the brain controlled special functions. He adhered to the belief in devils and accepted severe treatment for the mentally ill, but Willis is regarded as an outstanding physician and neuroanatomist of his time (6). His *Opera Omnia* (1681) is considered an excellent example of the development of neurology in the medical scene. There is much in it that deals with cerebral pathology, mania and melancholia, mental deficiency, and cerebral accidents. Willis discovered the eleventh pair of cranial nerves (6). As implied, his psychological perceptiveness did not match his general medical and neurological abilities. He is considered one of the men in the history of psychiatry to approach it in a manner that has been called a psychiatry without psychology (6). Yet Willis was able to focus on psychological behavior in a way to permit him to observe melancholic and maniacal states in the same individual, suggesting their combined existence in one illness. Actually, this awareness had existed for some clinicians during the Graeco-Roman period. The repetitive observation of the same or similar phenomena is not unusual in fields of medical and scientific areas of activity. Eventually the observations take hold firmly and are cemented into the basic structure of a body of knowledge. This was to occur toward the close of the nineteenth century in the case of manic-depressive psychosis.

The aforementioned stress on structure in relation to ideational and emotional aspects of functioning finds representation also, at the time of Willis, in the work of Vieussens (1641-1716) who considered the corpora striata the location of imagination. Medical emphasis was on the brain, with interest in certain aspects of mental deficiency, brain injury, cretinism, apoplexy, convulsive seizures, and paralysis. Problems that might be categorized as neuroses, character disorders, psychoses and borderline psychotic problems were usually not given careful attention. As Zilboorg says, the physicians were "wedded to physics, chemistry, and physiology."

There were other currents in motion at this time. Some overlapped the views given above. Others went beyond them and broadened the horizon of understanding and interest in human behavior and the psychological make-up of man.

René Descartes (1596-1650) was a French physician-philosopher categorized by Ackerknecht as an istrophysicist. He is usually identified as the person who ascribed to the pineal gland the seat of the rational soul. Although his writings are credited with an early exposition of reflex phenomena, they are also regarded as very speculative (3). Yet Boring, the historian of psychology, sees the work of Descartes marking the beginning of modern psychology, and he regards this philosopher-scientist as the Father of Physiological Psychology and Reflexology (7). And as for the pineal gland emphasis in relation to Descartes, Boring stresses that the idea of the soul encapsulated anatomically in this location is really a common misconception. In reality it was regarded as a center of interaction. Murphy, viewing these works also in historical perspective, focuses on the analysis of the emotions and points out that the "passions" are treated virtually as mechanical happenings with links to motion in the brain, the blood, the "spirits," and the vital organs. Emotions appear to be treated almost as intellectual functions (8). In the historical development of the concept of the "unconscious," the views of Descartes are associated with the idea of a "physiological unconscious" (9). Emphasis on the sense organs was notable in the Cartesian system and this emphasis was to be found also in the thinking of other philosophers of that time. Transformation of stimuli into thought, feeling, and behavior occurred in the brain (6). It was an organ for integration of the functions of mind and body. Mathematics was Descartes' tool for investigation of physical sciences. Introspection or self-observation was the means of focusing on consciousness (5).

During the seventeenth century we find Thomas Hobbes (1588-1679) agreeing with the Baconian opinion about knowledge stemming from experience. Furthermore, experiences are ascertained through external senses. Hobbes has been considered the first writer on mental phenomena to note that sensations are not always consistent with the nature of external objects (5).

Whereas a view of functioning akin to a physiological unconscious was ascribed to Descartes, the idea of a perceptive unconscious was linked to Gottfried Wilhelm Leibnitz (1646-1716). This mathematician and philosopher is believed to have offered the first clarification of an unconscious mental life (9). The concept of an apperceptive unconscious is related to Kant, and a vital unconscious with the German romanticists. As Ellenberger has pointed out, six concepts of this nature were discussed in a symposium published by Morton Prince (10), and in a more recent volume at least sixteen meanings of the word "unconsciousness" received attention (11).

Outside of Paris, in 1641, La Maison de Charenton was founded. It is called the oldest mental hospital in France, and after 1789 it was used entirely for the mentally ill (5). As for treatment at this time, we find "ducking" to have been used frequently as a psychiatric measure. It probably had some effectiveness as a shock technique involving an obvious punitive component that would not find favor today. Herman Boerhaave (1668-1738) suggested a twirling stool producing, through spinning, a state of unconsciousness in the patient. Presumably subsequent reorganization of mental functioning might encourage normality (12). The ducking and twirling methods are to be found from time to time in the course of psychiatric history. It has been suggested that the image of Boerhaave, the clinician and great teacher, as it was passed down to us through the years, may have been perpetuated considerably by appealing personality attributes instead of more impersonal general medical accomplishments (Schneck, 13).

At this time, Georg Ernst Stahl (1660-1734) was constructing a theory of animism (14). Physician and chemist, he viewed life as a product of the soul. The animistic concepts in opposition to materialism influenced eighteenth century psychiatric thinking (5). Vitalism pertained to man. Mechanistic forces operated in lower animals. The effort to ward off deleterious influence may lead to mental illness. The soul bears similarity to the Archaeus of Paracelsus, and life is motion stemming from the soul. Diseases are disorders of the soul (5). Concern with the "seat" of the soul and of mental illness had long been a quest of considerable interest. It was intensified at this time (6).

Stahl was born in Germany and served as a professor at Halle. Some historians regard him as a great pioneer in medicine and see him as having made a real attempt to bring physical and mental phenomena close together (6). Emotional influences on the course of somatic illness were recognized by Stahl in his theoretic concepts and practice. When the functions of the soul are interfered with, psychiatric illness ensues. Zilboorg tells us that Stahl's influence was small in Germany, greater in France, and that he was, in fact, rediscovered by Ideler about one hundred years after his death, when his *Theoria Medica Vera* was reissued during 1831-32 in a new German edition.

Stahl is identified also with his phlogiston theory, analyzing combusion as involving the escape of this particular substance, so named. It was a dominant concept up to Lavoisier's time. Ackerknecht comments that Stahl separated his medical and chemical interests and is credited with being a great chemist of his time (3). Sigerist acknowledges Stahl's significant place in the history of chemistry and remarks further that his following in medicine was based mainly on his outlook on disease showing connections with Sydenham's views while his animistic doctrine satisfied those who were in revolt against materialism. He points out aptly that Stahl's outlook would tend to foster the acceptance of vitalism and further the study of psychiatric issues (4).

Thoroughly identified with seventeenth century medicine is William Harvey's 1628 publication, *Exercitatio Anatomica de Motu Cordis et Sanguinis in Animalibus* (16). It was followed by a storm of protest and opposition. Harvey proposed his ideas on the circulation of the blood, but the microscopic identification of capillary connecting links had to await the efforts of Malpighi fifty years later. As happens from time to time, Harvey's medical practice dwindled after his famous contribution appeared. Reliability as a physician is questioned when proposals are made that are considerably in opposition to traditional thinking (15).

Before Stahl was to appear on the medical scene as an animist, Harvey was functioning as what Sigerist has termed a "consistent dynamist." Issue has been taken with the assertion that his clinical practice bore no significant differences from that of his colleagues. It is claimed that he took definite interest in the "signal influence of the affections of the mind" (17). Harvey's writings and anecdotes recorded by Sir Kenelm Digby and Robert Boyle have been used to show his approach to those aspects of medicine veering later toward the developmental directions of psychiatry and neurology. It has been claimed, in fact, that Harvey possessed a lifelong interest in facets of medicine which were to blossom out afterwards into neurology, psychiatry, and studies included under the term "psychosomatic medicine," with his writings foreshadowing some fundamental findings (18). As for Sir Kenelm Digby, attention has been called to his description of *folie à deux* more than two hundred years before Baillarger, Lasègue, and Falret, who have been identified with this psychotic reaction (19).

The seventeenth century witnessed also the contributions of the famous Thomas Sydenham (1624-1689) (20). He was probably the outstanding clinician of this period (21). Of great influence on many European men of medicine, he was also to be the inspiration of Benjamin Rush who contributed to the development of psychiatry in the United States (22). Singer has considered him the founder of modern clinical medicine (23). Lewis has already pointed out that Sydenham described hysteria in his *Dissertatio Epistolaris* issued in 1682 (5). He believed hysteria to be the most common of all chronic diseases. He recognized the existence of hysteria in men as well as women, and has specifically been credited with this observation although it had been made by others before him. For men, the diagnosis of hypochondriasis was substituted. The point has been made that association of morbid preoccupation over physical health with hypochondriasis was not evident in Sydenham's time, and that this view is apparently credited to Jean

Pierre Falret in 1822 (24). The impressive comment of Sydenham on hysteria reads as follows: "Of all chronic diseases hysteria—unless I err—is the commonest; since just as fevers—taken with their accompaniments—equal two thirds of the number of all chronic diseases taken together, so do hysterical complaints (or complaints so called) make one half of the remaining third . . . " (25).

Veith has made some interesting observations on the historical aspects of hysteria (24). She has noted that in 1618, Carolus Piso suggested the brain as the origin of hysteria so that the illness need not be considered as limited to women. Of greater appeal perhaps is her observation that persistent stress on the physical origin of hysteria may have spared numerous ill women from exorcism and torture during the Middle Ages.

It has been pointed out that varying diagnostic differences through the years are often confusing. Many of the phenomena identified with hysteria and hypochondriasis were apparently consistent with what today would be identified with a variety of reactions ranging from the neurotic and psychophysiologic to some types of psychotic reactions. Schizophrenic reactions would be included in the latter category, especially those identified recently as unclassified, latent, ambulatory, or pseudo-neurotic. Thus the point was made that in terms of present evaluations, the array of symptoms noted by Sydenham credit him with willingness to become aware of the widespread existence of psychological illness in general. This fact is pertinent in relation to modern times when attention is focused so acutely on the high percentage of psychological illness among patients seeking help in all medical specialties. Thus Sydenham appears to warrant recognition in a more significant way in the history of psychiatry. Apart from descriptions of hysteria and recognition of its existence in men, he voiced awareness of the very widespread occurrence of psychological illness during the years of active practice of clinical medicine (Schneck, 26, 35).

For some, Sydenham's ability in differentiating symptoms from disease exceeded the skill of Sauvages and Linné. At a later date, Pinel, like Sydenham, was to show interest in evaluating the common denominators in patients with similar types of illness (27).

One of Sydenham's students, the seafaring Thomas Dover, in his early years of medical practice in Bristol first used crude mercury for hysteria. The oral quicksilver had positive psychological effect therapeutically as concluded by his biographer, and seemed especially effective for patients with asthma (28).

Sydenham was friendly with the outstanding physician-philosopher, John Locke, author of *Essay Concerning Human Understanding*. A recent study shows the apparent influence of the two men on one another, contrary to the claim of Sydenham's biographer (20) that there was no trace of Locke's influence in Sydenham's work (29). It has even been claimed that Locke's clinical material on patients show him to be a more thorough disciple of Hippocrates than Sydenham, perhaps even more deserving of the title "English Hippocrates." Despite any element of truth, this is probably stretching a point. In any case there may be cause to suspect that Sydenham was influenced by Locke in the development of a more critical view in medicine. Locke's fallibilism has been defined as a view that one cannot achieve certainty in hypotheses on issues of fact because the mind does not have the ability to know the essences of things. This attitude was probably of influence on Sydenham who was not, as is true of Locke, a medical fallibilist from the onset of his career (29). The impact was especially pronounced on Sydenham's attitude toward theory. While Locke is not considered to have had much influence on the understanding of mental illness, Pinel in later years cited Locke as well as Condillac for his psychobiological outlook (6).

Another well known seventeenth century figure is Sir Thomas Browne (1605-1682) who has consistently been identified with a trial for witchcraft at which he testified. Medical histories have linked him with the conviction (21), and his great admirer, Sir William Osler, regarded his evidence as significant on this score (30). A recent biographer views the testimony as pertaining to witchcraft without direct implication of guilt or innocence of those concerned (31). This issue is generally the note on which Browne finds his way into comments which pertain in any way to psychiatric history.

Browne is the author of the celebrated *Religio Medici* which has fascinated so many readers during the three hundred years since its publication. A careful study of this work from the point of view of present psychiatric knowledge and concepts has elicited some points worth noting. There is no question about Browne's belief in the devil and in witches, but his knowledge about mental derangement transcended limited connections with demonology and was consistent with facts and experience available to physicians of his time and to those who preceded him. Of special interest, however, is the reflection, in many parts of *Religio Medici,* of astute and discerning insights into psychological experience and functioning (Schneck, 32). The essence of his observations have a remarkably modern sound and show awareness of dynamics of personality functioning, fine points of interpersonal relations, and subtleties of psychological experience which are being expounded and developed now in psychiatric practice and medico-psychological literature. The sum of his comments and reflections is impressive. Whereas *Religio Medici* has been referred to as a religious, spiritual, philosophical, and literary work (33), it is presented now as at least in part a psychological work in the modern sense, although not completely, of course, a psychological essay (Schneck, 32). His views have since been elaborated and incorporated into the currently expanding body of a psychology of personality. A variety of psychological dynamisms is to be found in his work. In modern descriptions they would be designated mechanisms of compensation, repression, reaction formation, identification, introjection, rationalization and displacement. Browne did not use the term "unconscious" but he was clearly aware of unconscious components in human behavior. The turmoil of inner contradictions was clear to him. Browne was obviously a perceptive physician with a keen and discerning mind. Study of the aforementioned work prompted the view that he deserves a more important niche in the history of psychiatry than that which he has thus far been accorded. It was felt also that he deserved further evaluation as a forerunner of present day psychologically minded doctors.

Browne's literary style has persistently aroused the curiosity and pleasure of readers. Some excerpts from his classic work convey its feeling:

"Hee that relieves another upon the bare suggestion and bowels of pity, doth not this so much for his sake as for his own: for by compassion we make another's misery our own, and so by relieving them, we relieve our selves also." Elsewhere we read, "Further, no man can judge another, because no man knowes himselfe, for we censure others but as they disagree from that humour which wee fancy laudable in our selves, and commend them but for what wherein they seeme to quadrate and consent with us." Later we find, "But how shall we expect charity towards others, when we are all uncharitable to our selves? Charity begins at home, is the voyce of the world, yet is every man his greatest enemy, and, as it were, his own executioner." As a final note, "Those have not only depraved understandings but diseased affections, which cannot enjoy a singularity without a Heresie, or be the author of an opinion without they be of a Sect also."

Whereas Zilboorg (6) credits Esquirol with use of the term "hallucinations" in its modern definition, the word itself is among those ascribed to Browne for coinage or popularization (31).

That Browne's psychological perceptiveness and intuitiveness was reflected not only in his famous classic could be demonstrated in an additional study. His *Letter To A Friend* and *Christian Morals* were found to add support to the claims and observations noted above. Many of his insights may be discovered in the writings of scholarly men such as some philosophers and novelists. Browne was a practicing physician and his psychological acumen must be viewed within the context of his basic life work. When seen this way, greater interest in him is merited from the vantage point of his place in the history of medical psychology. He was concerned about symbolization and other dream mechanisms, the psychopathology of senility, delusions, personality distortions in false accusations of witchcraft, aspects of super-ego functioning, externalization of conflicts, imitation and idealization, projection and many other psychological dynamisms, and problems in psychological maturation (Schneck 34). More of this aspect of Sir Thomas Browne will probably come to light in the future.

REFERENCES

1. Ehrenwald, J.: *From Medicine Man to Freud.* New York, Dell, 1956.
2. Olsen, A. J.: The Witches Still Ride. *New York Times Mag.* p. 38, Sept. 8, 1957.
3. Ackerknecht, E. H.: *A Short History of Medicine.* New York, Ronald Press, 1955.
4. Sigerist, H. E.: *The Great Doctors.* New York, W. W. Norton, 1933.
5. Lewis, N. D. C.: *A Short History of Psychiatric Achievement.* London, Chapman and Hall, 1942.
6. Zilboorg, G. and Henry, G. W.: *A History of Medical Psychology.* New York, W. W. Norton, 1941.
7. Boring, E. G.: *A History of Experimental Psychology.* New York, Appleton-Century-Crofts, 1950.
8. Murphy, G.: *Historical Introduction to Modern Psychology.* New York, Harcourt, Brace, 1949.
9. Ellenberger, H.: The Unconscious Before Freud. *Bull. Menninger Clin., 21*:3, 1957.
10. Prince, M.: *Subconscious Phenomena.* Boston, R. G. Badger, 1910.
11. Miller, J.: *Unconsciousness.* New York, John Wiley, 1942.
12. Stainbrook, E.: Shock Therapy: Psychologic Theory and Research. *Psychol. Bull., 43*:21, 1946.
13. Schneck, J. M.: Hermann Boerhaave and Samuel Johnson. *J. A. M. A., 161*:1414, 1956.
14. Menninger, W. C.: *Fundamentals of Psychiatry.* Topeka, Capper, 1943.
15. Stimson, D.: *Scientists and Amateurs, A History of the Royal Society.* New York, Henry Schuman, 1948.
16. Power, D'A.: *William Harvey.* New York, Longmans, Green, 1897.
17. Hunter, R. A. and Macalpine, I.: William Harvey, Two Medical Anecdotes. *St. Bartholomew's Hosp. J., 60*:200, 1956.
18. Hunter, R. A. and Macalpine, I.: William Harvey: His Neurological and Psychiatric Observations. *J. Hist. Med. & Allied Sc., 12*:126, 1957.
19. Greenberg, H. P., Hunter, R. A. and Macalpine, I.: Sir Kenelm Digby on "Folie A Deux", An Historical Note. *Brit. J. Med.*

Psychol., 29:294, 1956.

20. Payne, J. F.: *Thomas Sydenham.* New York, Longmans, Green, 1900.
21. Major, R. H.: *A History of Medicine.* Springfield, Thomas, 1954.
22. Goodman, N. G.: *Benjamin Rush.* Philadelphia, University of Pennsylvania Press, 1934.
23. Singer, C.: *A Short History of Medicine.* New York, Oxford University Press, 1928.
24. Veith, I.: On Hysterical and Hypochondriacal Afflictions. *Bull. Hist. Med., 30*:233, 1956.
25. Latham, R. G.: *Works of Thomas Sydenham.* London, Sydenham Society, 1848.
26. Schneck, J. M.: Thomas Sydenham and Psychological Medicine. *Am. J. Psychiat., 113*:1034, 1957.
27. Veith, I.: Psychiatric Nosology: From Hippocrates to Kraepelin. *Am. J. Psychiat., 114*:385, 1957.
28. Dewhurst, K.: *The Quicksilver Doctor, The Life and Times of Thomas Dover.* Bristol, John Wright, 1957.
29. Romanell, P.: Locke and Sydenham: A Fragment on Smallpox (1670). *Bull. Hist. Med., 32*:293, 1958.
30. Osler, W.: *Selected Writings of Sir William Osler.* London, Oxford University Press, 1951.
31. Finch, J. S.: *Sir Thomas Browne.* New York, Henry Schuman, 1950.
32. Schneck, J. M.: Sir Thomas Browne, Religio Medici, and the History of Psychiatry. *Am. J. Psychiat., 114*:657, 1958.
33. Denonain, J. J.: *Sir Thomas Browne, Religio Medici.* London, Cambridge University Press, 1955.
34. Schneck, J. M.: Psychiatric Aspects of Sir Thomas Browne with a New Evaluation of His Work. *Med. Hist.* (In Press.)
35. Schneck, J. M.: The Thomas Sydenham-Benjamin Rush Transition in the History of Psychiatry. *Med. Hist.* (In Press.)

Courtesy of the New York Academy of Medicine

FRANZ ANTON MESMER

Chapter 6

THE EIGHTEENTH CENTURY

Writings on the subject of mental illness increased during the eighteenth century as the specialty of psychiatry developed gradually into more concrete form. The physician concerned with this area of work usually engaged in the general practice of medicine (1). Sydenham and Browne serve as earlier examples. The usual orientation of the psychiatrically minded men of the time was essentially neurological. There continued to grow, however, an interest in the emotional life of patients, and simple correlations and observations ensued. Clément Joseph Tissot (1750-1826), for instance, showed such interests in his concern with connections between music and moods (1). Recently it has been implied that another man of this century with a similar name, Simon-Andred Tissot (1728-1797) had some recognition of functioning below conscious levels although it was probably unwarranted to have referred to him as a Freudian before Freud (2).

One of the outstanding men of this century, from the vantage point of historical perspective, was Franz Anton Mesmer (1734-1815). He engaged in philosophical studies at Dillingen and Ingolstadt, obtained a doctorate, and studied medicine later in Vienna. His graduation dissertation of 1766 is an item of interest because it was to point the way toward the later development of the concept of animal magnetism. The latter was to undergo alterations with the emergence and development of mesmerism, hypnotism and psychoanalysis, ultimately expanding into a dynamic psychiatry incorporating psychoanalytic concepts and techniques, with reemergence of hypnosis as an area of study involving complex ingredients in a total behavioral science (Schneck, 3, 4). In a scholarly evaluation of Mesmer's work, George Rosen, the medical historian, commented on his theory of animal magnetism (5). The themes involved in Mesmer's views seemed to be in keeping with certain theoretical concerns of the medical world of the eighteenth century. Disease as disharmony with disturbance of nervous fluid stemmed from ideas of dyscrasia and critical days of ancient humoral pathology. It was related to the irritability theory of Albrecht von Haller (1708-1777), and the excitation theory of John Brown (1735-1788).

In 1779, Mesmer published his famous *Mémoire sur la Découverte du Magnétisme Animal.* Only lately has it been translated into English (6). This work contains the historical twenty-seven propositions which read as follows:

"1. There exists a mutual influence between the Heavenly Bodies, the Earth and Animate Bodies.

2. A universally distributed and continuous fluid, which is quite without vacuum and of an incomparably rarified nature, and which by its nature is capable of receiving, propagating and communicating all the impressions of movement, is the means of this influence.

3. This reciprocal action is subordinated to mechanical laws that are hitherto unknown.

4. This action results in alternate effects which may be regarded as an Ebb and Flow.

5. This ebb and flow is more or less general, more or less particular, more or less composite according to the nature of the causes determining it.

6. It is by this operation (the most universal of those presented by Nature) that the activity ratios are set up between the heavenly bodies, the earth and its component parts.

7. The properties of Matter and the Organic Body depend on this operation.

8. The animal body sustains the alternate effects of this agent, which by insinuating itself into the substance of the nerves, affects them at once.

9. It is particularly manifest in the human body that the agent has properties similar to those of the magnet; different and opposite poles may likewise be distinguished, which can be

changed, communicated, destroyed and strengthened; even the phenomenon of dipping is observed.

10. This property of the animal body, which brings it under the influence of the heavenly bodies and the reciprocal action of those surrounding it, as shown by its analogy with the Magnet, induced me to term it *Animal Magnetism.*

11. The action and properties of Animal Magnetism, thus defined, may be communicated to other animate and inanimate bodies. Both are more or less susceptible to it.

12. This action and properties may be strengthened and propagated by the same bodies.

13. Experiments show the passage of a substance whose rarified nature enables it to penetrate all bodies without appreciable loss of activity.

14. Its action is exerted at a distance, without the aid of an intermediate body.

15. It is intensified and reflected by mirrors, just like light.

16. It is communicated, propagated and intensified by sound.

17. This magnetic property may be stored up, concentrated and transported.

18. I have said that all animate bodies are not equally susceptible; there are some, although very few, whose properties are so opposed that their very presence destroys all the effects of magnetism in other bodies.

19. This opposing property also penetrates all bodies; it may likewise be communicated, propagated, stored, concentrated and transported, reflected by mirrors and propagated by sound; this constitutes not merely the absence of magnetism, but a positive opposing property.

20. The Magnet, both natural and artificial, together with other substances, is susceptible to Animal Magnetism, and even to the opposing property, without its effect on iron and the needle undergoing any alteration in either case; this proves that the principle of Animal Magnetism differs essentially from that of mineral magnetism.

21. This system will furnish fresh explanations as to the nature of Fire and Light, as well as the theory of attraction, ebb and

flow, the magnet and electricity.

22. It will make known that the magnet and artificial electricity only have, as regards illnesses, properties which they share with several other agents provided by Nature, and that if useful effects have been derived from the use of the latter, they are due to Animal Magnetism.

23. It will be seen from the facts, in accordance with the practical rules I shall draw up, that this principle can cure nervous disorders directly and other disorders indirectly.

24. With its help, the physician is guided in the use of medicaments; he perfects their action, brings about and controls the beneficial crises in such a way as to master them.

25. By making known my method, I shall show by a new theory of illnesses the universal utility of the principle I bring to bear on them.

26. With this knowledge, the physician will determine reliably the origin, nature and progress of illnesses, even the most complicated; he will prevent them without ever exposing the patient to dangerous effects or unfortunate consequences, whatever his age, temperament and sex. Women, even in pregnancy and childbirth, will enjoy the same advantage.

27. In conclusion, this doctrine will enable the physician to determine the state of each individual's health and safeguard him from the maladies to which he might otherwise be subject. The art of healing will thus reach its final stage of perfection."

There are many points of interest in these propositions, including those ingredients of thought that were to develop later into more concrete concepts of suggestion in its manifold aspects, and complex issues of transference relationships. In the meantime, Mesmer, the Austrian physician, has become one of the most fascinating and controversial figures in the history of psychiatry. His work is frequently regarded as the beginnings of modern psychotherapy. He has been praised on one hand as a brilliant innovator, yet condemned too as a deliberate charlatan. His true significance probably has yet to be evaluated.

As has been mentioned earlier, trance states had been employed long before Mesmer's innovations in primitive and archaic cultures by magicians and by priest-physicians. Mesmer's theories were originally based on the belief in the efficacy of magnets which could cure disease when applied to afflicted parts of the body. He used them in this way, following intermittent traditional belief in their value. Later he substituted a wand or rod, and eventually as the idea of animal magnetism unfolded, the touch of the magnetizer was sufficient for therapeutic purposes. Patients could be treated in groups as they held iron rods immersed in a wooden tub, the *baquet*, which contained glass and iron filings. Many patients were helped and there is little doubt that symptomatic relief was probably obtained by psychiatric patients of numerous categories and patients with an array of somatic problems incorporating significant psychological components. Disagreements and pressures among groups with vested interests led to the appointment of the Royal Commission of 1784. This is probably the best known of several commissions that came into existence over the years. Its members included Benjamin Franklin (1706-1790); A. -L. Lavoisier (1713-1794), the distinguished chemist; J. -I. Guillotin (1738-1814) of guillotine fame; and A. -L. de Jussieu (1748-1836), the famous botanist. The report issued was essentially unfavorable, with certain exceptions. It seems that the role of psychological factors in results obtained was sensed by the observers, but surely not appreciated in terms of their real significance (Schneck, 7).

Convulsive movements or crises were often associated with the magnetization in Mesmer's technique. He may have been aware of the sleep-like trance state although it is usually associated with the findings of a disciple, the Marquis de Puységur, in 1784. About this time, a French physician, J. -H. -D. Pététin (1744-1808), described hypnotic catalepsy. Many other hypnotic phenomena such as hallucinations, posthypnotic suggestion, anesthesia and analgesia, had been encountered and described by 1825 (8).

Now turning elsewhere, in 1753 William Battie offered clinical demonstrations of psychiatric patients at St. Luke's Hospital for Lunatics, and based on this fact some have seen the beginning of psychiatry as a specialty in England (9). His views appeared in *A Treatise on Madness* (1758), and Hunter points out that Battie was one of the few psychiatrists to achieve the Presidency of the

Royal College of Physicians of London (10). Battie objected to the abuse of the mentally ill in their treatment as criminals or as annoyances to the general population. It was not long after this that Mesmer, in several countries on the continent, was declaring the value of animal magnetism, taking an interest in numerous patients with "nervous disorders," and apparently benefiting many as a result of treatment in his clinics. But, as implied already, many a negative note has been voiced about him. One of the most recent assertions has dealt with the aforementioned student graduation thesis of 1766, *Dissertatio Physico-Medica de Planetarum Influxu,* to which attention has been called with the purpose of analyzing it in relation to ideas developed into the theory of animal magnetism, and in an attempt to demonstrate that portions were plagiarized from Richard Mead's *De Imperio Solis ac Lunae in Corpora Humana et Morbis in de Oriundis* (11). Mead (1673-1754), the source of the ideas as alleged, was the very well known and successful eighteenth century British physician (12).

A study of these works suggested that Mesmer derived concepts of tides in the atmosphere from Mead, although acknowledgment of the source was not extended to him. There was, however, a reference to Mead elsewhere. It was said that Mesmer took almost verbatim a section from Mead which dealt with atmospheric tides. Some of his own ideas on gravitation were added. These findings and the usurpation of case histories was regarded as consistent with an implied lack of scholarship in Mesmer (11).

There are still other points of interest in connection with this period. In the mid-eighteenth century, a number of physicians were using treatment with electricity (13). Furthermore, about 1750, John Wesley obtained an electrical apparatus and in 1759 issued a publication on electricity. In these years "hundreds, perhaps thousands," of people were benefited by electrotherapy, it was claimed, and in 1767 Middlesex Hospital became the first teaching institution in London to purchase an electrical machine. St. Bartholomew's and St. Thomas's made such purchases afterwards (14). An "asylum" in Leicester possessed an electrical gadget for treatment of patients. In 1788 a treatment room was arranged especially for this purpose. By 1793, a London Electrical Dispensary was in process of organization. Within ten years more than three thousand patients were said to have been treated with one half cured and relief offered to the majority of the rest (14). The history of electrical applications for illness had long antedated this more organized effort and can be traced back to the use of the electric eel in Greco-Roman times.

It was during the years in the mid-eighteenth century when the electrotherapy movement was under way that Mesmer was developing his theory of animal magnetism and applying his therapeutic technique. A careful examination of his series of propositions elicits reference to electricity in numbers twenty-one and twenty-two. "This system will furnish fresh explanations as to the nature of Fire and Light, as well as the theory of attraction, ebb and flow, the magnet and electricity." Then, "It will make known that the magnet and artificial electricity only have, as regards illnesses, properties which they share with several other agents provided by Nature, and that if useful effects have been derived from the use of the latter, they are due to Animal Magnetism" (6). Mesmer interpreted his observations in the context of his own theoretical structures. The interpretation can be shifted easily to the area of preferred historical reevaluation that stresses the essential significance of the doctor-patient relationship with all that it implies psychologically, and the involved facets of suggestion in its complex forms. Of interest then is that Mesmer was probably still quite correct in the core of his discernments. The therapeutic effects of electricity and magnets were basically related to the same forces that promoted the operation of animal magnetism, theory excluded. Disregarding his theory still, the foregoing is quite consistent with present day observations where the psychological factors involved in the methods of electrotherapy continue to attract attention aside from the concurrent physiological studies. The psychological elements in therapeutic results with electrotherapy have, indeed, come in for considerable attention for quite a long time (16).

There is an additional point worth noting (Schneck, 15). Electrical appliances frequently elicit convulsive reactions of greater or lesser degree depending on a number of variables and related obviously in therapeutic situations to the intent of the physician. Mesmer, with what we would regard now as his psychotherapeutic approach, was obtaining convulsive reactions called crises in a number of his patients and these reactions were regarded as therapeutically beneficial. For some patients they must have had considerable psychological importance in terms of the dynamics of the illness itself. It may be significant to note that the presence or absence of convulsions in electrotherapy continues to be a point of discussion, even now, from the view of their physiological and psychological desirability as part of the therapeutic regime. The parallel may permit better evaluation in historical perspective at some future time. It bears special relation to the proposition expounded by Mesmer immediately following the two that have just been mentioned. We read, "It will be seen from the facts, in accordance with the practical rules I shall draw up, that this principle can cure nervous disorders directly and other disorders indirectly" (6).

Through the years Mesmer has been the subject of several biographical studies (17). Regardless of opinions about him as a person, historians concede his important place in the historical evolution of psychotherapy (18). His animal magnetism gave way to techniques referred to as Mesmerism, hypnotism, and the current concepts of hypnotherapy and hypnoanalysis. Among the men involved in some of these developments were Elliotson, Braid, Liébeault, Bernheim, Charcot, Janet, and Freud.

A point worth noting at this time is that stressed by Ackerknecht. It will stand out to some extent in the account of these developments. Significant achievements of eighteenth century medicine and science came to the fore in the second half particularly, and they appear to be linked with the philosophical movement of the Enlightenment (19). He regards separation of the first part from the preceding seventeenth century to be essentially artificial because the major themes continued past the demarcation, in addition to which they operated on a somewhat lower level. It will be seen later that difficulties in separating events and figures of the late eighteenth and early nineteenth centuries are encountered because the life spans of the contributors overlapped these periods and their contributions are in a sense identified with the turn of the century itself.

Identification of men with systems is not confined to Mesmer nor to physicians of earlier years. One such system has been linked to the well known William Cullen of Edinburgh (1712-1790) and its core is the "nerve force" as a basic element in life and disease (19). He has been considered a follower of Locke (18). Cullen was concerned with irritability of the nervous system and with endogenous aspects of mental disease. He was interested in such disorder as a pathological state of mind. Lewis mentions his work on paranoid features of mental diseases which he called "vesaniae."

One of Cullen's pupils was John Brown (1735-1788) who has been mentioned earlier as coming within the concurrent theoretical compass of the developments in animal magnetism. Brown's system made an impression in Germany, Italy, and the United States. Disease involved either sthenia which was caused by overstimulation, or asthenia, inability to react to stimulation (19). Therapeutic agents were used in an attempt to counteract such conditions by means of stimulating or depressing body functions. Opium and alcohol played a role in such treatment.

Early in this century, George Cheyne (1671-1743) was concerned with problems of obesity and with neurotic behavior which he termed "The English disease" (19). Robert Whytt (1714-1766) issued a book on hypochondriacal and hysterical reactions in 1764, and was an early proponent of experimental investigation in medicine (18).

The distinguished historian Max Neuberger rendered the opinion that the most enduring contribution of Johann Christian Reil (1759-1813) to psychiatry was his plea for the elimination of medieval maltreatment (20). Curiously, however, he sought improvement through fear, with the shock of firing cannon-shots, for example, or the traditional ducking in water. The straight-jacket and cowhide fit into this system. These came within his views of reasonable psychological methods of therapy (1).

A side-light on the theme of restriction of movement appears, in this connection, in an opinion on some clinical observations during the late eighteenth and early nineteenth centuries. These pertained to a seeming incompatibility between tuberculosis and insanity. A present-day writer looks at the history of the strait-waistcot in psychiatric therapy in the context of experimental studies on lung volume and the use of collapse therapy for tuberculosis. Insofar as this influence may have been brought to bear on afflicted patients, it might account, he feels, for reports on insanity more often halting the advance of pulmonary tuberculosis that the latter beneficially affecting the progress of insanity (21).

Reil thought of his treatment, mentioned above, as "noninjurious torture." Although Zilboorg cannot see him as a founder of rational psychology, he does point out that the basis of Reil's work lay in excellent knowledge of clinical medicine and psychiatry (1). He published *De Structura Nervorum* in 1796 and is regarded as important in the history of neurology. The "island of Reil" is named after him. He founded the *Archiv für die Physiologie* in 1796, was interested in patients' self-observations, and was attuned to the potential importance of ideational content. Descriptions of neurotic reactions are to be noted in his clinical data, and he revealed contact with depersonalization problems and dual personality. He possessed enlightened points of view on mental hospitals and considered in detail the problems of structure, organization, patient management, and socialization arrangements for the mentally ill (1).

Encompassing parts of the eighteenth and nineteenth centuries was the work of Johann Gottfried Langermann (1768-1832) whom Neuberger has credited as the first in Germany to separate in different hospitals those patients whom he regarded as curable and incurable. Langermann was concerned too about the psychological roots of somatic illnesses. Furthermore, he saw the need for systematic psychotherapy (20). In 1797 his doctor's dissertation was *On the Method of Recognizing and Curing Lasting Mental Diseases,* said to be his only publication in this area and, according to Kirchoff, the first psychiatric dissertation for a doctorate in Germany (1). Langermann was one of the well known figures in psychiatric history to oppose restraint and remove the strait jacket.

The periodic and yet at times persistent interest in non-restraint was illustrated further in Anton Müller (1755-1827) of Germany. Working with mental patients, he too stressed humane treatment and abolition of brutal restraint (1).

Another concurrent movement involved increasing social consciousness in general. As Ackerknecht puts it, the term "social science," appeared first, as no accident, in the publications of the Enlightenment (19). And Jean Colombier (1736-1789), physician in charge at the Hôtel-Dieu, was troubled by public apathy toward the plight of the indigent mentally ill (1).

We find also, at this time, the continued interest in classification, with the work of François Boissier de Sauvages (1706-1767), conservative and anatomically oriented in his outlook on mental illness. Yet he focused also on the "will" in its role in mental disorder (1). His nosological activities and his *Nosologie Méthodique* in particular, are reflections of his historical connections with Sydenham and Linńe. Mental aberrations fall into one of his ten categories of disease. As often as classification is stressed, so too does it come in for criticism. Both tendencies are frequently carried to extremes. Riese has reiterated its importance for order and generalization and its role in serving an economizing principle in our functioning (22). Its role of importance in science cannot be questioned seriously.

REFERENCES

1. Zilboorg, G. and Henry, G. W.: *A History of Medical Psychology.* New York, W. W. Norton, 1941.
2. Harms, E.: Simon-Andred Tissot (1728-1797), The Freudian Before Freud. *Am. J. Psychiat., 112*:744, 1956.
3. Schneck, J. M.: *Hypnosis in Modern Medicine,* 2nd Edition. Springfield, Thomas, 1959.
4. Schneck, J. M.: *Studies in Scientific Hypnosis.* Baltimore, Williams and Wilkins, 1954.
5. Rosen, G.: History of Medical Hypnosis. In Schneck, J. M.: *Hypnosis in Modern Medicine,* 2nd Edition. Springfield, Thomas, 1959.
6. Mesmer, F. A.: *Mesmerism, by Doctor Mesmer* (1779), Being the first translation of Mesmer's historic 'Mémoire sur la découverte du Magnétisme Animal' to appear in English, trans. by V. R. Myers with an Introductory Monograph by Gilbert Frankau. London, Macdonald, 1948.

7. Schneck, J. M.: Hypnosis. *American Peoples Encyclopedia* (*10*: 849). Chicago, Spencer Press. (In Press.)
8. Hull, C. L.: Hypnotism in Scientific Perspective. *Sc. Monthly, 29*:154, 1929.
9. Hunter, R. A. and Greenberg, H. P.: Sir William Gull and Psychiatry. *Guy's Hosp. Rep., 105*:361, 1956.
10. Hunter, R. A.: The Rise and Fall of Mental Nursing. *Lancet, 270*:98, 1956.
11. Pattie, F. A.: Mesmer's Medical Dissertation and Its Debt to Mead's De Imperio Solis ac Lunae. *J. Hist. Med. & Allied Sc., 11*:275, 1956.
12. Major, R. H.: *A History of Medicine.* Springfield, Thomas, 1954.
13. Stainbrook, E.: The Use of Electricity in Psychiatric Treatment during the Nineteenth Century. *Bull. Hist. Med., 22*:156, 1948.
14. Hunter, R. A.: A Brief Review of the Use of Electricity in Psychiatry. *Brit. J. Physical Med., 20*:98, 1957.
15. Schneck, J. M.: (In Manuscript).
16. Stainbrook, E.: Shock Therapy: Psychologic Theory and Research. *Psychol. Bull., 43*:21, 1946.
17. Goldsmith, M.: *Franz Anton Mesmer, A History of Mesmerism.* Garden City, N. Y., Doubleday, Doran, 1934.
18. Lewis, N. D. C.: *A Short History of Psychiatric Achievement.* London, Chapman and Hall, 1942.
19. Ackerknecht, E. H.: *A Short History of Medicine.* New York, Ronald Press, 1955.
20. Neuberger, M.: British and German Psychiatry in the Second Half of the Eighteenth and the Early Nineteenth Century. *Bull. Hist. Med., 18*:121, 1945.
21. Hunter, R. A.: Tuberculosis and Insanity. *St. Bartholomew's Hosp. J., 61*:113, 1957.
22. Riese, W.: History and Principles of Classification of Nervous Diseases. *Bull. Hist. Med., 18*:465, 1945.

Courtesy of the New York Academy of Medicine

Chapter 7

THE EIGHTEENTH CENTURY (Continued)

Cullen is said to have been the first to use the term "neurosis" as synonymous with nervous disease. His mental diseases or "vesaniae" were an order of the class neuroses (1). Neurosis was based on disturbance in motion and sensation, related to the nervous system, and was of universal rather than regional significance. According to Riese, here were the beginnings of the term "functional" although this term in its modern sense was to come into significance several decades later. Since the manifestations of disturbance were the primary consideration rather than anatomy or etiology, Cullen's classification has been linked to the physiological principle of classification traced to Galen. Later, Pinel was attentive to Cullen's work in this area (1).

There are other men and activities to be considered before attention is turned to Pinel. The work of John Haslam (1764-1844), for example, embraced the eighteenth and nineteenth centuries. Recently the claim was made that he has been unjustly neglected and this has been linked with concentration of late nineteenth century British psychiatry on evils of restraint. For Haslam asserted that the restraints employed in Bethlem were for the benefit of the patients (2).

Haslam's first book was *Observations on Insanity, with Practical Remarks on the Disease, and an Account of the Morbid Appearances on Dissection.* It was published in 1798, achieved success, and went into a second edition in 1809 under the title, *Observations on Madness and Melancholy.* Haslam's writings contained descriptions of the brain as it was studied in many autopsies. Zilboorg (3) has credited him with what appeared to be the first clinical description of general paralysis, but Leigh disagrees.

Haslam was clear in his descriptions, and cases of alcoholism, melancholia, puerperal psychosis, and schizophrenia are to be found. One case involving cortical atrophy is believed to come close to paresis, but the account as one recognizable under this heading is discounted (2). On the other hand it has been noted that Haslam observed alternating excitement and depression which, if continued, would imply an unfavorable prognosis. This stress on prognostic considerations is linked significantly to a late nineteenth century trend in psychiatry.

During the period under discussion, on the other side of the Atlantic, Benjamin Rush (1745-1813) was making his contribution to the care of the mentally ill. Bloodletting was in vogue and Rush was an outstanding exponent. To his excessive use of this treatment device were added the employment of emetics and purgatives. With European colleagues Rush accepted intimidation of some psychiatric patients for therapeutic purposes (3). Despite his shortcomings and some questionable practices, he carved out a secure niche for himself in the history of psychiatry. His biography attests to this (4) and his autobiographical data furnish many items of historical interest (5). For further details, a large number of his letters are available (6).

Like Sydenham to whom he has been compared, Rush was a clinician of broad experience. Sydenham was even surpassed by Rush according to the latter's friend Lettsom (7), but this opinion does not merit debate. Despite occasional objections (8), Rush is generally regarded as the Father of American Psychiatry. His major psychiatric publication will be mentioned later.

Whereas a recent historian has been lukewarm in his appraisal of Rush as a medical psychologist (9), his work and ideas have had great significance in the opinions of others. Shryock discerned his interest in personality and perceived Rush's anticipation of a modern orientation in psychiatry (10). These opinions included the belief that in his thinking about psychological issues, Rush's approach was dualistic. At the same time, Adolf Meyer (11), the distinguished psychiatrist, was evaluating his contributions including lectures on the Institutes and Practice of Medicine. Meyer was of the opinion that Rush saw "mind and body as a unit" and had awareness of "the unity of dynamics of disease." Rush was concerned with the functioning of the patient as an individual. The mind-body unity stressed by Meyer was in contrast to the dualistic philosophy credited to Rush elsewhere. Some of these points have been reemphasized by others (12). There appears to be a meaningful transition between Sydenham and Rush in views on psychological medicine (Schneck, 13). Sydenham recognized the widespread significance of psychological issues in the practice of clinical medicine. Rush was acquainted with Sydenham's work and acknowledged his indebtedness. He went beyond Sydenham in emphasizing the importance of psychology in general medical training, and he centered attention concretely on the study of the patient as an individual. The patient's psychological and physiological functioning were combined into a holistic pattern constituting a unitary view that is now experiencing more imperative emphasis in medical education.

Rush joined the medical staff of the Pennsylvania Hospital at the close of the American Revolution and he served for thirty years. This has been called the actual beginning of American psychiatry (14). He was much interested in psychiatric patients and tried to put the study and treatment of mental disease on a scientific plane it had not been accorded previously in this land. His theoretical concepts have not stood the test of time but his general efforts in this area of observation and education are commendable. He employed the tranquilizer, which was a chair for immobilization of the patient, and the gyrator, an additional treatment measure for disturbed patients. Lewis calls them "decidedly shock measures" (14). For this reason and because of their punitive implications, Rush has been criticized.

The history of mechanical restraint must take note of Vincenzio Chiarugi (1759-1829), the famous Italian physician concerned with treatment reform. He published a three volume work on insanity, removed chains and fetters at his hospital, St. Boniface, in Florence (1774-88), furthered the use of occupational therapy, strengthened sanitary techniques, and reenforced humane treatment for his patients (15). In many writings Chiarugi is barely mentioned, if at all, and his work has been overshadowed by the attention accorded Pinel. More recently, however, he has come in for more recognition (16). His attentive efforts on behalf of the mentally ill antedated the dramatic achievements of Pinel in France (17, 18). Lewis says he was the first in Italy and perhaps elsewhere to introduce a system of post-mortem studies on the brains of the mentally diseased (14).

Comparable movements occurred in the British Isles, for in 1792 William Tuke played a significant role in the establishment at York of the famous Retreat. Humane treatment included the removal of fetters and manacles. The whirling chair, plunge baths and similar measures continued in use in England, Scotland, and Ireland well into the nineteenth century (19).

Philippe Pinel (1745-1826) served as a physician at both the Bicêtre and the Salpêtrière. His work encompassed the period of the French Revolution and its aftermath, and the years of Napoleon as well. He has been described as conservative, adaptable, and courageous, and Zilboorg has recounted his work and accomplishments in detail (3). Pinel obtained a medical degree in 1773. The scientific, orderly, and logical, were of appeal to him. He translated Cullen's *Institutions of Medicine* into French (1785) and developed an interest in mental diseases, issuing publications in this field. One often encounters mention of Pinel's friend who became psychotic and died prematurely, this event having been allegedly a strong influence in his attraction to the problems of the mentally ill (20).

Pinel was appointed to the Bicêtre in 1793 and his removal of chains used unnecessarily for some patients was instituted gradually. He opposed the traditional view of punishment for the mentally sick and was bent on employing the simplest measures to enhance their betterment. On this score he has been compared with Johann Weyer (3). The removal of these chains has since become a highlight in psychiatric history, often glorified and glamorized. It has been claimed that without this achievement, the development of modern psychiatry would hardly have been possible (21). With this move, the role of reason was considered established in psychiatric treatment, and some have gone so far as to say that Pinel had, in fact, established psychiatry (22). Although such a claim is an exaggeration, much credit must surely be extended to the man and his work.

Pinel reorganized the administration at the Bicêtre, studied his patients carefully, and published scientific treatises. He made daily rounds, observed the behavior of his patients and made notes on their conversations. Zilboorg traces the introduction of psychiatric case records and histories to him (3). The systematic incorporation of this approach into mental hospital methods is believed to have had its impact more in the United States, especially at the turn of the present century, than in France and Germany. In this connection the special abilities and leadership of Adolf Meyer, August Hoch, and George H. Kirby at the New York State Psychiatric Institute have been noted (3).

While animal magnetism was proceeding in its historical development, and Benjamin Rush was active with his excessive bloodletting, Pinel was engaged in what has been called "moral treatment." This approach was in use by others at that time, and Lewis sees it as comparable in some ways to what has been termed "total push" in recent years. In his opinion the comparison is merited by the inclusion of psychotherapy, occupational therapy, and recreational therapy (23). Pinel objected to bloodletting as often practised, and he opposed indiscriminate prescription of drugs. In the course of moral treatment, as indicated, Pinel moved closer to his patients than did many other hospital physicians, and he was concerned about trying to understand the disease processes he encountered. This effort to achieve contact with the inner experiences of his patients prompts the view of him as a pioneer in the application of psychotherapy for the psychoses, a problem that has been attracting much attention recently (24).

Ackerknecht has referred to Pinel as the most prominent clinician of the first twenty years of the Paris clinical school, and he points out that Pinel suggested to his pupil Marie François Xavier Bichat (1771-1802) that he seek the core of some diseases in the body tissues (25). The tissue became for Bichat the basic unit in physiology, rather than the organ as had been the case with Morgagni. Vitalism had its impact on Pinel's thinking and activities. Bichat integrated a vitalistic physiology with anatomical work. He was much more impressed with the autopsy than with observation of symptoms, and Ackerknecht stresses Pinel's special interest in the latter as reflected in his classification of diseases. He refers to Pinel as essentially a man of the eighteenth century despite modernistic insights and feels that whereas Bichat died too young to establish his work in the new clinical medicine on a solid foundation, his teacher Pinel was incapable of taking this lead. On the relationship between Bichat and Pinel, Rosen has stated that it was the reading of the latter's *Nosographie Philosophique* (1798) which resulted in the important conceptions of tissue pathology that were developed further in *Traité des Membranes* (26).

Pinel was interested in the natural history of diseases. Riese, in his study of Pinel's medical thought and his views on human nature and disease, has translated Pinel's listing of frequent sources of physical and psychological illness: "A constitution, weak from the onset, or deteriorated through the excesses of youth, or still worse, through their perpetuation in the decline of life. The tremendous rise of man's ambitions, striving for honor, wealth, academic distinctions, fame, a sedentary life, detrimental to the secretions and muscular strength, while overeating and intemperance produce a hypersecretion of the nutritive juices, the numerous artificial stimulations of weakening functions, lack of sleep, overworking, excessive study, intense worries, never ending troubles, the turmoil of passions in families where tranquility, order and harmony should reign. . . . " (27). If this admixture points in any particular direction, it indicates Pinel's wish to see the totality of his patients' functioning including family, social, and occupational settings.

Riese credits Pinel with an early description of amnesic aphasia when, as a result of careful observation and history taking on a patient, he observed the ability to recognize objects with concurrent loss of memory for their names. The defect was purely nominal (28).

Reverting once more to the issue of restraint with which Pinel's name has become irrevocably associated, we may point out again that expression of concern about it keeps recurring through the years. Even today the subject continues to be studied and discussed. Only lately with reference to a declaration by John Conolly who was to come after Pinel in the history of this movement, its pertinence was believed to require reenforcement. This declaration places restraint and neglect in the same category and considers them substitutes for "the thousand attentions needed by a disturbed patient" (29).

While progress was being made in these aspects of psychiatric development, other issues were unfolding in the sphere of thinking about mental functioning. The seventeenth century philosopher and mathematician, Wilhelm Leibnitz (1646-1716), has been credited with the first clear formulation of unconscious mental functioning, but his view seemed to place the concept of threshold at a zero point with the conscious above and unconscious below. The threshold appealed to Johann Friedrich Herbart (1776-1841), philosopher and psychologist, but for him it was an area with an array of changing perceptions and representations in conflict with one another (30). Leibnitz is associated with the establishment of the idea of psycho-physical parallelism although others, including Spinoza, had dealt with the theme of parallelism before him. Herbart is viewed by many, including the historian of psychology, Boring, as a dynamic psychologist in the advance from Leibnitz to Freud (31). As will be seen later, the continuum in this line of development was to include still other ingredients.

REFERENCES

1. Riese, W.: The Pre-Freudian Origins of Psychoanalysis. *In Science and Psychoanalysis.* New York, Grune and Stratton, 1958.
2. Leigh, D.: John Haslam, M.D.—1764-1844, Apothecary to Bethlem. *J. Hist. Med. & Allied Sc., 10*:17, 1955.
3. Zilboorg, G. and Henry, G. W.: *A History of Medical Psychology.* New York, W. W. Norton, 1941.
4. Goodman, N. G.: *Benjamin Rush.* Philadelphia, University of Pennsylvania Press, 1934.
5. Rush, B.: *The Autobiography of Benjamin Rush* (Edited by G. W. Corner). Princeton, Princeton University Press, 1948.
6. Butterfield, L. H.: *Letters of Benjamin Rush.* Princeton, Prince-

ton University Press, 1951.

7. Abraham, J. J.: *Lettsom.* London, William Heinemann, 1933.
8. Casamajor, L. J.: Notes for an Intimate History of Neurology and Psychiatry in America. *J. Nerv. and Ment. Dis., 98*:600, 1943.
9. Roback, A. A.: *History of American Psychology.* New York, Library Publishers, 1952.
10. Shryock, R. H.: The Psychiatry of Benjamin Rush. *Am. J. Psychiat., 101*:429, 1945.
11. Meyer, A.: Revaluation of Benjamin Rush. *Am. J. Psychiat., 101*:433, 1945.
12. Wittels, F.: The Contribution of Benjamin Rush to Psychiatry. *Bull. Hist. Med., 20*:157, 1946.
13. Schneck, J. M.: The Thomas Sydenham-Benjamin Rush Transition in the History of Psychiatry. *Med. Hist.* (In Press).
14. Lewis, N. D. C.: *A Short History of Psychiatric Achievement.* London, Chapman and Hall, 1942.
15. Deutsch, A.: *The Mentally Ill in America.* New York, Columbia University Press, 1946.
16. Bromberg, W.: *Man Above Humanity.* Philadelphia, J. B. Lippincott, 1954.
17. Shryock, R.: The Beginnings: From Colonial Days to the Foundation of the American Psychiatric Association. In Hall, J. K.: *One Hundred Years of American Psychiatry.* New York, Columbia University Press, 1944.
18. Castiglioni, A.: *A History of Medicine.* New York, Knopf, 1941.
19. Power, D'A.: *Medicine in the British Isles.* New York, Paul B. Hoeber, 1930.
20. Bettmann, O. L.: *A Pictorial History of Medicine.* Springfield, Thomas, 1956.
21. Rogers, F. B.: Pinel: Pioneer Psychiatrist. *Phila. Med., 53*:1123, 1957.
22. Winkler, J. K. and Bromberg, W.: *Mind Explorers.* New York, Reynal and Hitchcock, 1939.
23. Lewis, N. D. C.: Historical Roots of Psychotherapy. *Am. J. Psychiat., 114*:795, 1958.
24. Reik, L. E.: The Historical Foundations of Psychotherapy in Schizophrenia. *Am. J. Psychoth., 10*:241, 1956.
25. Ackerknecht, E. H.: *A Short History of Medicine.* New York,

Ronald Press, 1955.

26. Rosen, G.: The Philosophy of Ideology and the Emergence of Modern Medicine in France. *Bull. Hist. Med., 20*:328, 1946.
27. Riese, W.: Philippe Pinel, His Views on Human Nature and Disease, His Medical Thought. *J. Nerv. and Ment. Dis., 114*:313, 1951.
28. Riese, W.: The Early History of Aphasia. *Bull. Hist. Med., 21*:322, 1947.
29. Jacoby, M. G., Babikian, H., McLamb, E. and Hohlbein, B.: A Study in Non-Restraint. *Am. J. Psychiat., 115*:114, 1958.
30. Ellenberger, H.: The Unconscious Before Freud. *Bull. Menninger Clin., 21*:3, 1957.
31. Boring, E. G.: *A History of Experimental Psychology.* New York, Appleton-Century-Crofts, 1950.

Chapter 8

THE NINETEENTH CENTURY

The turn of the century saw the gradual development of the phrenological movement. It has been pointed out often that the father of this movement, Franz Joseph Gall (1758-1828) was a very capable anatomist and neurologist, although for many people the field of phrenology is associated with a questionable technique of personality evaluation based on skull configuration. The medical historian, Owsei Temkin, refers to Gall as the godfather of the principle of cortical localization of mental faculties (1). The basic issue in his work pertained to the cerebral cortex as the physical substrate of the mind. It was a mosaic of organs and each possessed a psychological function. These views are believed to have had a helpful influence on growing knowledge about the anatomy and physiology of the brain (2). As another historian has put it, Gall intended his phrenology to be a psychophysiology (3). Each of a variety of mental functions depends on its proper area in the brain. An excess in a particular function is related to an enlargement in an area of the brain, and the overlying bone of the skull is correspondingly enlarged. It can be seen how this could stimulate investigations of localization of brain functions, but it is clear too that popular interest can readily be excited, and in fact did result. Opportunists moved rapidly into this area of concern (4). This circumstance lent itself to a degrading of Gall's efforts. Along with other professional difficulties, despite his basic worthiness, Gall encountered problems in academic acceptance. The result eventually was neglect of his efforts in psychology and physiology (5).

The term "phrenology" was adopted by Spurzheim (1776-1832) who was associated with Gall in the historical developments in this area. Spurzheim, however, was a propagandist rather than a scientist. In developing his concepts, Gall referred to physiognomy and craniology as descriptive terms (3).

In discussing aphasia as a disorder in symbolic thought and expression, Riese has made reference to Gall who has been credited with the first complete description of this condition in association with a wound of the brain. Reference is made also to Gall's recognition of speech disorder in connection with a vascular lesion. Riese noted that the first description involving the fundamentals of aphasia was actually offered by Goethe. Furthermore, Gall was not the first medical author to present the features of aphasia. Philippe Pinel did this in his *Traité Médico-Philosophique sur l'Aliénation Mentale*. One may find still additional studies on early descriptions of aphasia (29).

For a while, in the nineteenth century, the history of phrenology overlapped that of mesmerism, and for many the two interests became peculiarly associated. This applied to popular views in particular, but it registered similarly for some in the medical profession as illustrated in the group associated with aspects of the work of John Elliotson in England. This development, as it applies to mesmerism, will be taken up later.

In the meantime, John Haslam, whose work has already been mentioned in part, continued his psychiatric efforts into the nineteenth century and published *Illustrations of Madness* in 1810. It contained an account of John Tilly Matthews, a patient at Bethlem. This publication has been considered an excellent clinical description of a case of paranoid schizophrenia, superior to reports prepared earlier by others. A present day student of Haslam believes he has been neglected by medical historians and considers him the most original and perceptive of writers in the field of psychiatry between 1798 and 1828. In addition to descriptions of schizophrenia, he presented material on obsessional neuroses and manic-depressive reactions (7). Leigh has called him the first contributor in English to the area of forensic psychiatry. He clearly favored "moral management" of the mentally ill and he was recognized in France, Germany, and the United States (7).

While Pinel did remove chains from his hospitalized patients, Haslam's supporter regards the act as essentially a gesture because his writings do make reference to restraint and coercion so that his practices differed little from those of Haslam. The latter is supported as the more solid contributor despite the fame accorded Pinel. It is believed that perhaps Haslam's personality worked to his detriment. This involved the tendency toward "biting comments" about other psychiatrists, some questionable writings and attitudes about reformers, and other elements which apparently, despite his abilities, made him difficult to get along with (7).

The issue involving Haslam and Pinel touches on the question of priority which crops up repeatedly in the course of medical history. Wartenberg has offered pertinent observations on this score (8). Not often is it possible to trace a disease, sign, or reflex to a particular writer because several possibilities are usually available. The selection may have to do with an initial description, or with an individual who appreciated the true significance of his observations. It may relate to the person who first intimated its presence or to the observer who supplied a definite outline or correct explanation. As an example, Wartenberg mentions that the well known Babinski sign was described before him by Remak in 1893 and by Marshall Hall in 1841, fifty-five years prior to Babinski. These observations will be found to be pertinent for a number of events already described in this history and they will apply also to happenings yet to be outlined. Wartenberg's observations have been elaborated by others (30).

Returning now to Benjamin Rush, we find his productive work continuing into the early nineteenth century. His major psychiatric effort, *Medical Inquiries and Observations upon the Diseases of the Mind,* was published in 1812. This book is often regarded as his most important scientific contribution (9). It was the first general volume on psychiatry in America and the only textbook of its type which continued to be of influence for more than half a century (10). There had been two publications by Englishmen which were issued prior to Rush's book. One was *View of the Nervous Temperament* by Thomas Trotter. It was reprinted at Troy, New York, in 1808. The other was *Practical Observations on Insanity* by Joseph Mason Cox. It was issued in Philadelphia in 1811 (11). Yet, unwilling to accept Rush as the Father of American

Psychiatry, Casamajor felt that it would be as meaningful to think of him as the father of American physiotherapy because of his tranquilizer and gyrator in their alleged therapeutic applications. He cited Dorothea Dix, to be discussed later, as perhaps more the Mother of American Psychiatry, and William Hammond as more the Father of American Neurology (12). Rush has been attacked even more pointedly. He has been condemned as a menace in the sick-room with the added note that to regard his work as among the medical classics is to be guilty of myth-making (13).

Despite such occasional opinions, Rush was indeed the most famous physician of his time. He was a graduate of Edinburgh and a signer of the Declaration of Independence. During the American Revolution he was involved in difficulties with William Shippen, Jr. in connection with medical administration in the military forces. Shippen has taken his own place historically as a pioneer in American medical education (14). Rush's charges against Shippen were quite serious. A military historian considered Rush a poor subordinate (15).

Ackerknecht sees Rush as more of an eighteenth century systematist than a follower of Sydenham. As he puts it, Rush offered a variation of John Brown's system by reducing the number of diseases from two to one (16). Throughout his career, Rush was energetic and active. He worked extremely hard at all times, especially stress periods such as the yellow fever epidemic of 1793 in Philadelphia. He became the best known of the American anticontagionists. Active politically, Rush was also in the forefront of a variety of movements for social improvement. So great was his presence that it has been said it exceeded the unusual influence of Sir William Osler on his colleagues (17).

Rush's psychotherapy was consistent with his personality attributes and intellectual forcefulness. Both his sincerity and his moralistic tendencies came to the fore in contact with patients (18). His general psychiatric methods were believed to be consistent with his theories. Thus, blood-letting matched his idea that the cause of mental disease was related to the blood vessels in the brain. When the brain was overcharged with blood, it was proper to deplete the body of such blood even to the degree of inducing faintness and debility (18). In his letters containing professional advice, there is to be found also the role of religious or psychiatric advisor (19).

When Benjamin Rush died, he left in one of his children, James Rush (1786-1869), the most original American psychologist of the nineteenth century (20). Roback speaks of him also as the first behaviorist, an opponent of metaphysical thinking, and an author of a system of thought based on objectivistic principles.

The thread of animal magnetism and mesmerism may be picked up at this point. Mesmer has been called a typical rationalist and speculative systematist of the eighteenth century (16). The influences he set in motion developed significant ramifications. The interest in animal magnetism reached its height on the continent between 1820 and 1840. Then it shifted to England for two decades, finally returning to the continent, especially to France, toward the close of the century (Schneck, 26).

The outstanding figure identified with this area of investigation at that time was John Elliotson (1791-1868), a famous and capable physician. He is often claimed to be the earliest doctor to have encouraged the use of the stethoscope in England. He was of much significance in advancing the application of mesmerism in medical practice (21). There is no doubt about his merit and abilities as a clinician (22). He was popular with his students, excelled as a writer, and enjoyed great success (23). Mesmerism as a subject for investigation and demonstration became increasingly controversial as did Elliotson as a physician and teacher. As pressure was brought to bear more and more, he resigned as Professor of the Practice of Medicine at the University of London.

For thirteen years Elliotson and his supporters issued a publication, *The Zoist: A Journal of Cerebral Physiology and Mesmerism, and Their Applications to Human Welfare.* It included numerous articles on the therapeutic efficacy of the mesmeric state in a variety of medical problems and for surgical anesthesia. During the course of Elliotson's work, a demonstration was arranged under special circumstances by the medical reformer, Thomas Wakley. The results were confusing to proponents of mesmerism but satisfying to Wakley who had serious doubts about Elliotson's claims. Insufficient psychological knowledge and intuitiveness on the part of both men compounded the confusion, but the questions that arose were of sufficient importance in instilling doubts at the time to result in this demonstration serving as a turning point historically for this period of mesmeric study. Wakley, founder and editor of the *Lancet,* was involved repeatedly in controversies and legal entanglements (24). Many prominent men of the time, Astley Cooper for example, and Abernethy of St. Bartholomew's came into conflict with him (25). Elliotson was only one of his targets in high places. Controversies notwithstanding, Elliotson was invited to deliver the Harveian Oration for 1846. To be sure, he spoke on mesmerism, delivering the lecture in Latin and arranging for simultaneous publication in Latin and English, thus obtaining greater publicity (27). One of the results of this period in the mesmeric movement, according to Rosen (28) was that its advocates for use in surgery were able to focus attention on painless operations, thus assisting in the eventual acceptance of ether and chloroform (28).

Elliotson felt that psychological disorders were poorly understood and treated improperly with a variety of medications. He was of the opinion that mesmerism could be helpful for these illnesses. Drawing attention to neuroses in this way has been considered a significant step for mesmerism in its role in the history of psychotherapy (31).

While Elliotson was involved with his work in England, James Esdaile (1808-1859) was developing further the use of mesmerism for purposes of surgical anesthesia. Much of his work centered on natives in India where he performed more than 300 major and minor surgical operations. In 1846 he issued his classic publication, *Mesmerism in India, and its Practical Application in Surgery and Medicine.* During the course of these studies, Esdaile was able to consider the potentialities of hypnotic subjects, and he took an interest in their psychological functioning. For example, he commented on mesmeric dreaming from the view of planning, problem solving, sudden insight, and creative experience. From intellectual and cultural vantage points, his subjects were few in number for experimentation in such psychological spheres. Probably inadequate orientation on his part in psychological theory and background precluded additionally any systematic observations he might otherwise have made (Schneck, 32).

James Braid (1795-1860), also a surgeon, practiced in Manchester, England. Originally skeptical of mesmerism, he developed considerable interest in it, established its validity, searched for physiological explanations of some phenomena, and eventually incorporated concepts of suggestion into his findings. He is credited with introducing the term "hypnotism" and some of its derivatives into our nomenclature. In 1843 he issued his views in *Neurypnology, or the Rationale of Nervous Sleep.* Boring tells us that the word "hypnosis" was to appear in the 1880s rather than in Braid's publications although it appeared during the preceding decade in medical literature when connected with narcotic sleep (3). Zilboorg speaks of the birth of psychotherapy in connection with Braid, and later Liébeault, as a unique event in the history of medicine (31). The importance of these happenings was not limited to the issue of a special technique. Rather it lay in the new paths open to scientific investigation of the neuroses, bringing them more and more into the area of psychiatry and paving the way for a broader view of the field of mental illness. Peculiarly enough, this role of hypnosis, inadequately appreciated then, continues to be insufficiently grasped even today. On the other hand, a positive note true of hypnosis by the 1880s continues true today with considerably enriched possibilities. It is a method of treatment with complex variations and adaptations, a method of research, and itself a subject for research (Schneck, 34).

In the meantime, that kindly, retiring country doctor in Nancy, France, A. A. Liébeault (1823-1904), was using hypnotherapy extensively. In 1866 he published a book, *Du Sommeil et des Etats Analogues, Considerés Surtout au Point de Vue de L'Action de la Morale sur Le Physique,* which is said to have had only one copy sold until Liébeault was joined later by the medical professor, H. Bernheim (1837-1919). Bernheim helped to popularize his colleague's contributions and therapeutic success with a variety of illnesses. Bernheim himself was later the author of the classic *La Thérapeutique Suggestive,* issued in final form in 1886. Their studies emphasized the psychological, suggestive, and therapeutic aspects of hypnosis, and in conjunction with the efforts of other colleagues their nucleus has been called the Nancy School. Contrasting with their outlook was that of Jean Martin Charcot (1825-1893), the distinguished neurologist who worked with his students and colleagues at the Salpêtrière. The Salpêtrière or Paris School stressed the physical aspects of hypnosis, the view of hypnosis as a pathological phenomenon, and the use of magnets and metals in influencing the hypnotic state. Treatment possibilities through hypnosis were minimized. These opinions were based heavily on the efforts of Charcot's co-workers of whom Alfred Binet (1857-1911) and Charles Féré (1857-1907) are linked in their publication of the well known book, *Animal Magnetism* in 1888. In that year Féré discovered bodily electrical phenomena associated with emotion (5). Binet and Théodore Simon are associated with the famous intelligence tests bearing their names. Many of the observations of the Paris School have not withstood the test of time and the group diminished in stature when compared with the Nancy School. Another group, not as well known or referred to often as such, is the School of the Hospital de la Charité. Its leader was the neuroanatomist, Jules Bernard Luys (1828-1897). Luys made many significant contributions to the field of neurology and assumed a secure place in its historical development (33). The Charité School parallelled the Salpêtrière in its experimental and physicalist approach. It held therapeutic and suggestion concepts at the same time which leaned more toward the Nancy School. Fundamentally it was closer, however, to the Charcot faction and it appeared to retain post-mesmeric fluidist concepts (Schneck, 35).

During this period, hypnosis was being investigated in some way by one group or another, or by some formally constituted commission. It has been pointed out that one of the outstanding features of the history of hypnosis is the series of such commissions established specifically for purposes of critical investigation. The issue of commissions is of historical importance because they influenced strongly the general attitudes toward the subject under investigation. This pertained not so much to the content of reports, but to the influence of the attitudes of the appointing bodies toward conclusions reached in the reports. Generally, appointing bodies tended to accept unfavorable decisions with the rejection of favorable findings. This is of interest in connection with what may be called the history of scientific attitudes (Schneck, 36).

The Charcot group was popular and authoritative. As such it possessed considerable influence in exciting concern with hypnosis and in furthering the study of neuroses (31). As has been said often, Charcot made hypnosis respectable (37). Associated with this general movement was Joseph François Félix Babinski (1857-1932) whose view of hysteria, which he termed "pithiatisme," entailed the idea of its manifestations being induced by suggestion and removed by countersuggestion (38).

Charcot is closely identified with those clinicians who proclaimed the importance of clinical observation. He has been regarded as perhaps the most representative clinician of his time (16). During this period, concepts of the unconscious continued to unfold, reaching a high point in the work of Freud toward the close of the century. Pierre Janet (1859-1947) was part of this movement. Earlier, Henry Maudsley in England had been commenting that consciousness was not coextensive with mind, and he had noted that much associated with mind was not easily accessible through introspection (3).

For Charcot, hypnosis was essentially an experimental neurosis. Although his orientation was neurological and neuroanatomical, he was aware of elements of suggestion in studies of hypnotic pheonmena. Despite this awareness, many of the findings of his group of workers did not hold up well. Many claims have been made to account for this. For example, it has been pointed out that his subjects were few in number and these were repeatedly used for demonstration purposes with inadequate precautions to avoid improper influences that would negate the validity of allegedly controlled experimentation. In a recent biography, the view is offered that Charcot's assistants developed these hypnotic subjects for experimentation and demonstration. As a result, Charcot was not as aware as he should have been of the deficiencies that existed under these circumstances (39). What might appear to be a well meant effort at exoneration is of questionable benefit because it serves more as a poor reflection on his clinical astuteness in this area of study.

Bernheim had, at this time, much interest in the theme of suggestibility and its role in the behavioral attributes of people in general as opposed to those classified specifically as suffering from hysteria. This research brought him into contact with a wide range of disorders constituting the psychoneuroses. His attempt to gain insight into human behavior through this approach has been regarded as the first known effort to seek a psychopathological basis for understanding of behavioral motivations (31). He was also the first scientific psychologist to stress the irresistible impulse concept in legal psychiatry, but its reception by legal authorities recalled the efforts and problems of Johann Weyer (31).

Pierre Janet (1859-1947), a meticulous psychopathologist, is often seen as having failed to overcome the view of hysteria as degenerative. Consistent with this is his reference to its symptoms as stigmata (3). He is credited with initiating the trend to bring clinical and academic psychology together in the development of meaningful concepts. During his years of work, Janet accumulated a vast quantity of clinical observations and psychological data. He was impressed with the automatic quality of functioning in neurotic behavior, and saw the role of unconscious elements in hysterical reactions, but it is often said that his view of the latter was perhaps limited in its dynamic ingredients. Zilboorg made the particular point that Janet admitted using the word "unconscious" as a *façon de parler.* He also indicated of Janet that his psychological treatment methods were essentially environmental and persuasive. On the other hand he was impressed by Bernheim's approach to the treatment of hysteria as de-suggestive rather than suggestive, with the particular willingness to see the ingredient of this view as revealing Bernheim to be "the true forerunner" of Freud.

Boring has pointed out Janet's special influence on Morton Prince (1854-1929) in particular. Prince, who is so closely associated with concepts of multiple and co-conscious personalities, was Janet's contemporary. Founding the Harvard Psychological Clinic in 1927 furthered the effort to bring together clinical and academic psychology. The clinical heritage retained its influence for William James (1842-1910) who, in his major psychological work, made use of the efforts of Charcot, Janet, and Binet (40).

Sigmund Freud (1856-1939) spent most of his life in Vienna and died in London. His early professional work was in neurology and he made contributions of good quality. Electrotherapy became part of his practice in treating the neuroses but in this he was disappointed. In 1885 Freud spent some time in Paris with Charcot and in 1889 he observed some of the work of Bernheim and Liébeault. His view of Bernheim's experiments on hospital patients impressed him with the possible existence of strong forces at work within patients while hidden from consciousness (41). In Vienna, Freud came into contact with Josef Breuer (1842-1925), a respected general practitioner who had been working with hypnosis in connection with the neurotic problems of some of his patients. Their collaboration in this hypnotherapeutic endeavor played a significant role in the origin and development of psychoanalysis. This early work pointed up in particular the cathartic method involving spontaneous verbalizations and discharge of emotions during the hypnotic state. In 1893 their co-authored paper appeared and it dealt with the mechanisms of hysterical phenomena. In 1895 the classic, *Studien Uber Hysteria* was published (42). In this connection Zilboorg has stressed that it was the first occasion in the history of medical psychology that a therapeutic device, while attempting to remove the cause of illness, proceeded to the discovery of the cause itself (31). Regarding this issue of "cause," however, it must be kept in mind that concepts are in process of alteration continually, and historical perspectives on this score are changing already.

As Freud continued his studies, he believed he found it necessary to discontinue the use of hypnosis. The development of psychoanalysis was already under way. The reasons for discontinuing the use of hypnosis were outlined by him, but it has been felt that certain personal needs required satisfaction in this move, and the objective reasons may not have been completely valid. One of the issues that has been examined in this regard deals not only with transference, but with problems of countertransference which Freud was to explore more fully in the course of subsequent studies. In any case his decision was clearly a significant point in the history of psychoanalysis, of hypnosis, and of psychiatry. One remarkable blind spot is the failure to assess properly in historical perspective the fact that the objections to hypnotic technique at that point were gradually eliminated in time as a result, interestingly enough, of what was largely learned subsequently through Freud's psychoanalytic endeavors. The impact of the emotional reliance on tradition in this area has been discussed from the historical vantage point (Schneck, 43) and a more involved examination of Freud and hypnosis has appeared recently (44).

A final point on this phase of the history of medical psychology relates to Joseph Breuer. A very brief autobiographical manuscript was developed in 1925. Oberndorf has centered attention on it, with particular reference to Breuer's modest comment about his association with Freud and psychoanalysis (45). "In 1880 I had observed a patient suffering from a severe hysteria, who in the course of her illness displayed such peculiar symptoms as to convince me that here a glimpse was being offered into deeper layers of psychopathological processes. The insights then gained were presented by S. Freud and myself, first in a short preliminary study and later in the *Studies On Hysteria* by Breuer and Freud. This book, which was rather unfavorably received at first, went into its fourth edition last year. It is the seed from which psychoanalysis was developed by Freud."

REFERENCES

1. Temkin, O.: Gall and the Phrenological Movement. *Bull. Hist. Med., 21*:275, 1947.
2. Bailey, P. and von Bonim, G.: Evolution of the Cerebral Cortex: Organ of the Mind. *What's New, 198*:13, 1957.
3. Boring, E. G.: *A History of Experimental Psychology.* New York, Appleton-Century-Crofts, 1950.
4. Winkler, J. K. and Bromberg, W.: *Mind Explorers.* New York, Reynal and Hitchcock, 1939.
5. Murphy, G.: *Historical Introduction to Modern Psychology.* New York, Harcourt, Brace, 1949.
6. Riese, W.: The Early History of Aphasia. *Bull. Hist. Med., 21*:322, 1947.
7. Leigh, D.: John Haslam, M.D.—1764-1844, Apothecary to Bethlem. *J. Hist. Med. & Allied Sc., 10*:17, 1955.

8. Wartenberg, R.: On Neurologic Terminology, Eponyms and the Lasègue Sign. *Neurology, 6*:853, 1956.
9. Major, R. H.: *A History of Medicine.* Springfield, Thomas, 1954.
10. Lewis, N. D. C.: *A Short History of Psychiatric Achievement.* London, Chapman and Hall, 1942.
11. Overholser, W.: Cox and Trotter—Two Psychiatric Precursors of Benjamin Rush. *Am. J. Psychiat., 110*:825, 1954.
12. Casamajor, L. J.: Notes for an Intimate History of Neurology and Psychiatry in America. *J. Nerv. and Ment. Dis., 98*:600, 1943.
13. Robinson, V.: *The Story of Medicine.* New York, Albert and Charles Boni, 1931.
14. Corner, B. C.: *William Shippen, Jr., Pioneer in American Medical Education.* Philadelphia, American Philosophical Society, 1951.
15. Ashburn, P. M.: *A History of the Medical Department of the United States Army.* Boston, Houghton Mifflin, 1929.
16. Ackerknecht, E. H.: *A Short History of Medicine.* New York, Ronald Press, 1955.
17. Flexner, J. T.: *Doctors on Horseback.* New York, Garden City Publishing Company, 1939.
18. Bromberg, W.: *Man Above Humanity.* Philadelphia, J. B. Lippincott, 1954.
19. Butterfield, L. H.: Benjamin Rush: A Physician As Seen in His Letters. *Bull. Hist. Med., 20*:138, 1946.
20. Roback, A. A.: *History of American Psychology.* New York, Library Publishers, 1952.
21. Williams, H.: *Doctors Differ.* Springfield, Thomas, 1952.
22. Rosen, G.: John Elliotson, Physician and Hypnotist. *Bull. Inst. Hist. Med., 4*:600, 1936.
23. Clarke, J. F.: *Autobiographical Recollections of the Medical Profession.* London, J. & A. Churchill, 1874.
24. Sprigge, S. S.: *The Life and Times of Thomas Wakley.* London, Longmans, Green, 1897.
25. Brock, R. C.: *The Life and Work of Astley Cooper.* Edinburgh, E. & S. Livingstone, 1952.
26. Schneck, J. M.: *Hypnosis in Modern Medicine,* 2nd Edition. Springfield, Thomas, 1959.
27. Bishop, W. J. and Poynter, F. N. L.: The Harveian Orations, 1656-1947, A Study in Tradition. *Brit. Med. J., 2*:622, 1947.

28. Rosen, G.: Mesmerism and Surgery, A Strange Chapter in the History of Anesthesia. *J. Hist. Med. & Allied Sc., 1*:527, 1946.
29. Hoff, H. E., Guillemin, R. and Geddes, L. A.: An Eighteenth Century Scientist's Observation of His Own Aphasia. *Bull. Hist. Med., 32*:446, 1958.
30. Kaplan, E. B.: The Genesis of an Eponym. *Bull. Hist. Med., 32*:451, 1958.
31. Zilboorg, G. and Henry, G. W.: *A History of Medical Psychology.* New York, W. W. Norton, 1941.
32. Schneck, J. M.: James Esdaile, Hypnotic Dreams, and Hypnoanalysis. *J. Hist. Med. & Allied Sc., 6*:491, 1951.
33. Krieg, W. J. S.: Jules Bernard Luys (1828-1897). In Haymaker, W.: *The Founders of Neurology.* Springfield, Thomas, 1953.
34. Schneck, J. M.: *Studies in Scientific Hypnosis.* Baltimore, Williams and Wilkins, 1954.
35. Schneck, J. M.: The School of the Hospital de la Charité in the History of Hypnosis. *J. Hist. Med. & Allied Sc., 7*:271, 1952.
36. Schneck, J. M.: The First and Second Husson Commissions for the Study of Animal Magnetism. *Bull. Hist. Med., 27*:269, 1953.
37. Wechsler, I.: Jean Martin Charcot (1825-1893). In Haymaker, W.: *The Founders of Neurology.* Springfield, Thomas, 1953.
38. Wartenberg, R.: Joseph François Félix Babinski (1857-1932). In Haymaker, W.: *The Founders of Neurology.* Springfield, Thomas, 1953.
39. Guillain, G.: *J.—M. Charcot, 1825-1893, Sa Vie—Son Oeuvre.* Paris, Masson et Cie, 1955.
40. Morris, L.: *William James.* New York, Charles Scribner's Sons, 1950.
41. Freud, S.: *An Autobiographical Study.* New York, W. W. Norton, 1952.
42. Breuer, J. and Freud, S.: *Studies on Hysteria.* New York, Basic Books, 1957.
43. Schneck, J. M.: Countertransference in Freud's Rejection of Hypnosis. *Am. J. Psychiat., 110*:928, 1954.
44. Kline, M. V.: *Freud and Hypnosis.* New York, Julian Press and The Institute for Research in Hypnosis Publication Society, 1958.
45. Oberndorf, C. P.: Autobiography of Josef Breuer. *Int. J. Psycho-Analysis, 34,* Part 1, 1953.

Chapter 9

THE NINETEENTH CENTURY (Continued)

In evaluating psychiatry during the nineteenth century, it is well to pause and focus attention on observations by Lewis regarding scientific method (1). It is an issue of concern to anyone who gives serious thought to developments in medicine, clinical and experimental, and it is a theme that has been expounded repeatedly in scientific and general intellectual circles. Many conceptions and misconceptions have to do with the popular image of the scientist and how he functions. James B. Conant has written significantly on this subject (2, 3).

Lewis has outlined certain steps in scientific method: observations and a record of them; organization and classification of data with notation of similarities and differences plus and effort to separate the superficial from the basic; generalizations for the purpose of ascertaining underlying principles and the formulation of working hypotheses and tentative theories; application of experimental techniques within the framework of the hypotheses; attempts at interpretation. In some areas of study experimentation is difficult and there is hesitancy to apply the term "science" to these fields of investigation. As is mentioned frequently, if such hesitancy applies to psychiatry, it might be questioned in connection with geology and paleontology. Lewis believes that in place of experimentation it would be proper to substitute critical analysis and comparisons. Some investigators deeply concerned with science question whether there is truly any scientific method in fact. Furthermore, as Lewis has indicated, discovery is rarely through scientific method. The latter is a means of testing ideas and concepts. For comparisons with methods of work of some of our psychiatrist pioneers, reference may be made to the thinking, investigations and achievements of students in other fields of medical exploration, Paul Ehrlich (4), Claude Bernard (5), and later Frederick Banting (6) serving as examples. For psychiatry, the nineteenth century was to a great extent a descriptive period with studies of reaction types and attempts at classification (1). It was also a time of erecting hospitals, founding societies, publishing books, and issuing periodicals. It was a period when psychiatry took shape as a separate specialty in medicine and, as Zilboorg has pointed out, a significant item in the cultural development of Europe and the United States (7).

The *Annales Médico-Psychologiques* appeared in 1843, the *Allgemeine Zeitschrift für Psychiatrie* in 1844, the *American Journal of Insanity* also in 1844, and the *Journal of Nervous and Mental Disease* in 1874. In England the Medico-Psychological Association was on the scene in 1841, and in the United States the American Psychiatric Association appeared in 1844 under its initial name, Association of Medical Superintendents of American Institutions for the Insane.

It was early in the nineteenth century, 1818 specifically, that J. C. Heinroth apparently first used the term "psychosomatic" although combinations of psyche and soma with their derivatives had appeared from time to time (8). The most intensive evaluation of the more basic implications of psychosomatics has found expression, however, only during the past few decades (9). In a recent evaluation of early historians of psychiatry, Heinroth is pointed up as having offered the first large survey of previous psychiatric developments in his *Lehrbuch der Stoerungen des Seelenlebens* (1818) (10). He was interested in psychotherapy and has been called a universal scholar (38).

Zilboorg has used Guillaume Ferrus (1784-1861) as an example of a psychiatrist of the first half of the nineteenth century with characteristic aspects for that period (7). Ferrus worked under Pinel at the Salpêtrière. He became a physician in 1804, saw military service in the Napoleonic forces, and joined Pinel in 1818. He visited hospitals in France and England, realized the paucity of mental institutions, observed the poor conditions under which patients lived, and commented on the mixing of the interred criminal population with the psychotic patients. Ferrus was a pioneer in occupational therapy. He put patients to use on a farm and dairy and kept them beneficially employed in workshops. These activities blossomed further in the development of this trend as part of treatment in the private and State hospitals established later in the United States (7). In his own country this movement was less lasting at the time.

Ferrus brought clinical teaching to the Bicêtre where he had become physician-in-chief in 1826. He was interested in criminology, prison reform, and legal psychiatry. He was a founder of the Société Médico-Psychologique and served as its first president. He was considered a kind physician, deeply interested in the humane treatment of patients. With this reputation he could afford to be outspoken in his criticism of "purely idealistic" ideas concerning non-restraint. The term was used by John Conolly (1794-1866) in England.

From 1839, Conolly treated patients at the Hanwell Asylum without the use of mechanical restraints and in 1856 he published his book, *The Treatment of the Insane Without Mechanical Restraints*. It was greeted with skepticism, as Sigerist has shown (11). Conolly had developed early an interest in psychiatry and tried unsuccessfully to incorporate its teachings into the curriculum at the University College in London where he served as Professor of Practical Medicine. His influence on Sir William Gull has been pointed out, and the latter's reforms at Guy's Hospital, among other contributions, have been linked to this connection (12). Conolly's introduction of the non-restraint movement of this period spread throughout Europe and America. Another proponent of abolition of restraint was Robert Gardiner Hill (1811-1878) who opposed restraint in any form. He served as chief surgeon at Lincoln Asylum and then at the private mental hospital, Eastgate House (7). Significant in this connection is the account by Ferrus of viewing a patient held down by four strong guards in a padded cell in Conolly's hospital.

During this period, concern with humane treatment of the mentally ill found expression in the work of Biagio Miraglia (1814-1885) at the mental hospital of Aversa near Naples in Italy. When active there, it has been said that his methods required physical restraint for only two or three patients among a total of eight hundred, with a claim that more adequate space and personnel might have permitted complete removal of such restraint among this patient population. Miraglia was a proponent of "moral" therapy in addition to the medications prescribed for structural pathologic changes and physiological disturbance (13). He was interested in phrenology although not in a simple, "servile" fashion as a follower of Gall and Spurzheim. He was a thinking, active investigator who published the first Italian journal devoted completely to psychiatry, and founded the first association of Italian psychiatrists, Società Frenopatica Italiana.

Miraglia's efforts incorporated techniques which have been considered meaningful precursors of current group psychotherapy procedures. He made attempts to have patients participate in performances of dramatic presentations (14). Johann Christian Reil, who has been discussed earlier and whose work antedated Miraglia, was concerned with psychodramatic measures. He gave thought to the idea of plays specifically written for patients to suit their therapeutic requirements, with such patients participating as actors or observers (15). Incidentally, it may be mentioned that the brain area called the "Island of Reil" is believed to have been first described by Gall (1).

The interest in brain localization, common at the time, was shared by Ferrus to whom we now return. He was curious about constitutional predisposition in mental illness. As for treatment of patients, his attentiveness and concern with kindness found expression in his ability to be outspoken as, for example, in his criticism of patient management at the Gheel colony for the mentally ill, the pride of Belgium. He described the cruelty he had observed there (7). His orientation has been termed one of scientific eclecticism.

From time to time, including the present, we hear the claim that the psychiatrist must indeed love his mentally ill patients to be of aid to them. The assertion may perhaps be interpreted in different ways and some may deny its validity or find fault with the generalization. In any case this view is linked with Jean E. D.

Esquirol (1772-1840) who continued the traditions of Pinel and his achievements at the Salpêtrière, and is stated to have prepared the foundations of French psychiatry (17). Bromberg refers to his *Des Maladies Mentales Considérées sous les Rapports Médical, Hygiénique et Médicolegal,* published in 1838, the first modern treatise on clinical psychiatry. Esquirol's greatness, according to another historian, is rooted in a non-dogmatic attitude (17). He reorganized the French hospital administration and established in 1817 the first psychiatric teaching clinic in Paris. He played a responsible role in spreading interest in the function of daily medical rounds and in careful record keeping. He claimed a place in introducing the use of the stomach tube as a life-saving measure for patients who persistently declined food. For the feebleminded he was not able to offer any optimistic outlook, but his pupil, Séguin (1812-1880), was able to demonstrate to him various favorable changes after intensive treatment (1). Esquirol was concerned with emotional elements in psychological illness. He was among the earliest clinicians to use statistical approaches in evaluating his clinical records. He defined a concept of monomania, studied depressive reactions carefully and used the term "hallucinations" in the modern sense (7). Also, he introduced the term "remission" into psychological case descriptions (1).

The clinical tradition established by these masters of French psychiatry, with their descriptive efficiency, interest in structural pathology, and concurrent humane treatment efforts, were to continue for many years to find expression in the work of their followers. Examples of this heritage appear in Georget (1795-1828) and Fodére (1764-1835). E. J. Georget was only twenty-five years old when his major publication, *De la Folie* was issued. The idea of a unitary concept of mental disease was of interest to him. The underlying feature was evidently a brain disease which manifested itself in a variety of forms. Whether one fundamental disease existed or whether mental disease consisted of many separate illnesses was a point of issue in Germany more than in France during the nineteenth century (7). The theme itself is not outmoded today. And as for the patient's psychological status, the view of his contact with reality and his life of fantasy aroused the curiosity of men like the aforementioned Fodére.

Another pupil of Esquirol, Jean Pierre Falret (1794-1870), was interested in patients with depressions and suicidal drives, a problem which is today the focal point for much serious study. His *De l'Hypochondrie et du Suicide* was published in 1822. Furthermore, the alternating manic and depressive states came to his attention and he was able to separate the disturbance from other reactions, issuing his views under the title, *De la Folie Circulaire.* For Baillarger it was *folie á double forme* and toward the close of the nineteenth century it was delineated by Kraepelin as manic-depressive psychosis. Baillarger (1809-1890) studied patients with hallucinations, observed those occurring between sleep and waking referred to as "hypnogogic," and noted alcoholic hallucinations (7).

In the meantime, several clinicians were moving closer to the ultimate clarification of general paresis and Baillarger shared in this along with Falret and Delasiauve (1804-1893). The descriptions of J. L. Calmeil (1798-1895) were important in this respect, and Henry takes recognition of the fact that A. L. J. Bayle (1799-1858) engaged in a series of clinical studies of importance in this area (7). In 1822 Bayle affirmed that the pertinent somatic and psychological symptoms were an expression of one disease in particular, and he thought it was based on chronic inflammation of the meninges. Henry says that Bayle was the first to present general paralysis as a disease characterized by disturbance of intellectual functions, peculiar grandiose ideas, progressive muscular incoordination and enfeeblement. Furthermore it was asserted that general paralysis was not a complication of other mental illnesses and that the constellation of symptoms was not connected with other such illnesses (7). These observations furthered attempts to seek brain lesions in a variety of mental illnesses and many impressions of structural change were reported after post-mortem examinations although they did not prove especially helpful in promoting better understandings. Further clarification of general paralysis was produced later by the clinical experimentation of Krafft-Ebing (1840-1903) who, as Zilboorg has indicated, established the relationship between general paralysis and syphilis before the introduction of the Wasserman reaction. For many, the developments in connection with general paralysis and its structural components led to a turning away from a more pervasive interest in the psychological components of mental disease.

One of the pieces to form part of the pattern designed by Kraepelin toward the close of the century as the picture of dementia praecox, was supplied by Morel in 1850. This particular term was proposed by Morel to describe certain reactions appearing in youth and progressing toward ultimate deterioration. In later years it was observed increasingly that not all of the reactions apparently appeared in youth and many did not advance to the point of deterioration (18). Morel (1809-1873) was aware of the lag in psychological studies as contrasted with anatomical. He was interested in the history of mental diseases (with E. Lasègue), medico-legal issues, goiter and cretinism. The influence of Claude Bernard on Morel is said to have been considerable (5, 7). With his concern about degeneration, he saw mental disease as related largely to the result of hereditary weaknesses. Zilboorg states that with Morel's death the leadership in psychiatry in Europe passed from France to Germany (7). Attention to the psychology of the psychoses was shared by Renaudin (1808-1865) who saw mental disease as the expression of a breakdown in the coordinated relationships of feeling, understanding, and acting.

A variety of the interests and attitudes and ways of functioning as described in connection with some of the aforementioned psychiatrists were found among an even larger number of whom Magnan (1835-1916) might serve as one example. He had contact with Baillarger and Falret, studied general paralysis as did others of this period with an interest in structural defects, functioned as a neuropathologist and hospital administrator, and was concerned with medico-legal issues. Beyond this he studied various drugs, was especially interested in alcoholism, and, with Morel, was attracted to Prichard's concept of "moral insanity" which will be taken up later (7). With the growing interest in issues of restraint at that time, we find also that Magnan removed the camisole and other binding methods at St. Anne. At this time too, Lasègue was showing concern about *délire des persecutions,* and Magnan was interested in periods of incubation, persecution, and dementia.

As one historian has put it, the approach to what eventually came to be called schizophrenia was taking a Hippocratic turn, with attention to form, course, and outcome (7).

What has been described as the typical psychiatrist in France during this period possesses a counterpart in the description of a typical English psychiatrist. The example in Daniel Hack Tuke (1827-1895) has been delineated in detail by Zilboorg who say that what Tuke's life represented professionally for England had its American counterparts for this period. Furthermore, as an individual, Tuke possessed a unique place in the English speaking world as far as the history of medical psychology was concerned (7). Daniel H. Tuke was born in York. His great-grandfather, William Tuke, had founded the York Retreat in 1792. He worked for a while as a steward at the hospital during his early adult years before going on to studies in London and a medical degree at the University of Heidelberg. As his career blossomed, he showed himself to be a methodical man and a careful observer. As a physician he returned to the York Retreat. He was free in comparing ideas and experiences with colleagues at home and on the Continent. Tuke and George Savage assumed the editorship of the *Journal of Mental Science*. His psychiatric views have been described as enlightened eclecticism. He was engrossed in care of patients within the hospital setting and their aftercare following discharge. When writing about him, Zilboorg felt that Tuke's influence on English psychiatry was such that no one of similar stature had yet appeared after him.

Tuke's great-grandfather, William Tuke, showed leadership in the trend exemplified in France by Pinel. At the York Retreat, as Henry has reaffirmed, mechanical restraints were not often used, and stress was placed on kind, personal attention to patients, with exercise, and employment to suit the needs of the patient (7). When Hill, who has already been mentioned, went to the Lincoln Asylum, he encountered an institution which, opened in 1820, possessed in its early years a collection of strait-waistcoats, padded iron collars, heavy leather muffs, belts with manacles, iron wrist-locks, and jointed iron leg-locks (7).

William Tuke was a layman. His role was considerable in

the reform of the conditions under which the mentally ill lived and were treated. The York Retreat set a precedent which influenced the milieu of some hospitals established later in the United States. It has been said that what William Tuke did in England, Eli Todd did in New York (19). The Bloomingdale Hospital was an early example. The tradition established by Tuke was carried forward by his son Henry and grandson Samuel. They too were laymen. In the United States, aside from Bloomingdale, there were the Friends' Asylum of Frankfort and the Hartford Retreat (19). There, the humanitarian heritage bore further fruit. Bromberg (16) has made a point of the gradual change during the nineteenth century of reference from "madhouse" to that of "asylum". It seemed to parallel greater acceptance of therapeutic effort, and to reflect a more humane approach. The total picture of this period was more complex, however. In 1885 Daniel Hack Tuke reported on his study of institutions when he published *The Insane in the United States and Canada.* He considered John P. Gray a strong defender of mechanical restraint, and he saw British psychiatrists regarding the views of Hill and Conolly as "pious opinion" (19).

While the developmental trend in attitudes toward restraint may be traced historically, it is important that we recognize certain difficulties in evaluations. There are different types of restraint and varying degrees of restraint. The use of the term "nonrestraint" may possess varying relevancy. For example, in connection with the aforementioned Friends' Asylum in Frankfort, Henry points out that, as the second oldest in the United States dedicated to the mentally ill, it was the first in which a chain "was never used for the confinement of a patient." He adds that this does not imply the complete elimination of restraint because leather was substituted for iron (7). Significantly he comments further that here as well as in other hospitals there was a tendency to substitute solitary confinement for mechanical restraint.

In recent years there has been considerable discussion and disagreement about methods of treatment divided into the "physical" and the "psychological." Also there is controversy about so-called short-term and long-term approaches. One writer has referred to a trend toward short-term physical treatment, pointing up a comparison with what he regards as the greater psychological orientation in treatment offered by the nineteenth century pioneers in American psychiatry (20). A better look at this background takes us to the origins of the American Psychiatric Association. It has rightfully been said that the history of medical psychology in the United States during that century is the history of the American Psychiatric Association and the work of Dorothea Dix (7). The latter will be mentioned again soon. Zilboorg has also claimed that until the 1840s, no one had reached the stature of Benjamin Rush.

The American Psychiatric Association was founded in 1844 as the Association of Medical Superintendents of American Institutions for the Insane. Between 1893 and 1921 it was called the American Medico-Psychological Association. Its beginnings stemmed from discussions of Samuel B. Woodward (1787-1850) of Worcester State Hospital (Massachusetts) with Francis T. Stribling of Western State Hospital (Staunton, Virginia). These talks led to a meeting in Philadelphia attended by "The Original Thirteen." Aside from Woodward and Stribling, the founding group included Isaac Ray, John S. Butler, Samuel White, Charles H. Stedman, Pliny Earle, Thomas S. Kirkbride, Luther V. Bell, William M. Awl, John M. Galt, Amariah Brigham and Nehemiah Cutter. Albert Deutsch, who prepared a history of the mentally ill in America, remarked that "not the least striking feature" about the founders was their youth. This feature holds true often for the leaders of new movements and the proponents of new ideas. Perhaps in such matters youth is simply noticed more.

Although some of the founders are better known than others, it would be difficult and in any case unnecessary to decide degrees of merit in their contributions. Winfred Overholser believes Kirkbride has achieved greater fame than the others since his name was associated with the type of hospital construction prevalent among mental institutions throughout the country. His biography was written by Earl D. Bond (23).

Pertinent facts about the phrenological movement have already been covered. Its height, in the field of medicine, was reached during the first half of the nineteenth century, and its influence spread from Europe to the United States. The impact of phrenology on American psychiatry occurred near mid-century and it has been shown that most of the founders of the American Psychiatric Association were influenced by phrenological concepts in their thinking about neurophysiology, psychiatry, and psychotherapy (24).

In 1847, not long after the formation of the American Psychiatric Association, the *American Journal of Insanity* was able to report the first appointment of its kind at a medical school in the United States. Samuel M. Smith became Professor of Medical Jurisprudence and Insanity at the Willoughby University, Columbus, Ohio. He brought to his post previous psychiatric experience at a mental hospital (25). Also at this time, 1848 specifically, Pliny Earle (37) published his *History, Description and Statistics of the Bloomingdale Asylum for the Insane* (27). Statistical records and reports had not until then been of much concern in mental hospital administration. Despite its merits, many of the conclusions would not now be regarded as valid (26). Earle's account was a study of admissions from June 1, 1821 to December 31, 1844. In 1843 Amariah Brigham (1798-1849) became the first superintendent of the first New York State Asylum for the Insane at Utica. Statistical data were included in the first report. They pertained to movement of patients, monthly admissions, ages on admission, condition, occupation, nativity, residence, and causes of insanity. This material established a pattern followed by other institutions (26). The history of State Hospitals would constitute a significant part of the history of psychiatry in the United States. Occasionally, studies appear which deal with regional areas (28). The humane spirit which characterized the work of some of the psychiatrists in France and England was found also among many in America. Brigham serves as an example. He is credited with supervising among patients an active program that would be referred to now as occupational and recreational therapy. This work was of special merit and is believed to have been duplicated only in recent times (29, 30). Brigham founded and edited the *American Journal of Insanity* which has continued as the *American Journal of Psychiatry*. Edward Mead founded the second American psychiatric periodical, the *American Psychological Journal*. This publication lasted only through six issues of its first year (31).

Another of the founders of the American Psychiatric Association, William M. Awl (1799-1876), served not only as its second president, succeeding Woodward, but also as one of the original members and a vice-president of the American Medical Association. Awl is believed to have made the first suggestion in this country that schools be established for idiots and imbeciles (32). In France, J. M. G. Itard had been a pioneer in the study of such patients and had passed this interest on later to Séguin (21).

With increased attention in recent years to problems of forensic psychiatry, it is Isaac Ray (1807-1881), among the founders group, who has been receiving a relatively large share of notice. Ray is said to have been able to see the deficiencies of the social order of his time and to have had the ability and intention to act on them. Much of his work, as has been claimed for others, was influenced by the social pressures of the period (33). In 1838 he published *A Treatise on the Medical Jurisprudence of Insanity*. This is now a classic. It is Ray's best known work, is still called upon today, and stands out as a curious achievement of a man who showed evidences of extensive reading while engaged in rural practice having only occasional contact with psychiatric patients. This publication contains reformist views and an unusual account of medico-legal problems (34). Ray's contribution in 1863, *Mental Hygiene,* is one of the earliest occasions on which this term was used. "Ray's mania" is a phrase encountered only occasionally. It has reference to "moral insanity" described by others (36).

Regarding the aforementioned *Treatise,* an item worth stressing is its use by the defense counsel in the famous trial of Daniel M'Naughten "with the most telling effect" (35). In this trial of 1843 at Old Bailey criminal court for the murder of Edward Drummond, secretary to Sir Robert Peel, M'Naughten was found not guilty on the ground of insanity and the case is said to be the first in which medical science was used in direct opposition to ancient legal authority. The assassination attempt had actually been leveled at the Prime Minister, Peel, when his secretary was killed. There was strong opposition from many quarters to the results of this trial. The celebrated M'Naughten's Rules stemmed from this event and have remained to this day of prime importance in forensic psychiatry. Recently they have been subjected to much criticism. Diamond has supplied an entry dated March 21, 1854, from the Bethlem Hospital record of M'Naughten (35).

"He is a man of so retiring a disposition and so averse to conversation or notice of any kind that it is very difficult even for his attendant to glean from him any information as to his state of mind or the character of his delusions, but one point has been made, that he imagines he is the subject of annoyance from some real or fanciful being or beings; but more than this is not known for he studiously avoids entering into the subject with anyone. If a stranger walks through the gallery, he at once hides in the water closet or in a bedroom, and at other times he chooses some darkish corner where he reads or knits. His crime created great commotion at the time. In mistake for the late Sir Robert Peel he shot Mr. Drummond as he was going into the Treasury or some Government office and at that time imagined that the Tories were his enemies and annoyed him. He has refused food and been fed with the stomach pump."

While Isaac Ray and others in the medical profession played important roles in the forefront of the humanitarian movement, laymen too contributed their share. Outstanding among them was Dorothea Lynde Dix.

REFERENCES

1. Lewis, N. D. C.: *A Short History of Psychiatric Achievement.* London, Chapman and Hall, 1942.
2. Conant, J. B.: *Modern Science and Modern Man.* Garden City, Doubleday, 1953.
3. Conant, J. B.: *On Understanding Science.* New Haven, Yale University Press, 1947.
4. Marquardt, M.: *Paul Ehrlich.* New York, Henry Schuman, 1951.
5. Olmsted, J. M. D. and Olmsted, E. H.: *Claude Bernard and the Experimental Method in Medicine.* New York, Henry Schuman, 1952.
6. Stevenson, L.: *Sir Frederick Banting.* Toronto, Ryerson Press, 1946.
7. Zilboorg, G. and Henry, G. W.: *A History of Medical Psychology.*

New York, W. W. Norton, 1941.

8. Oberndorf, C. P.: *A History of Psychoanalysis in America.* New York, Grune and Stratton, 1953.
9. Kaplan, H. I. and Kaplan, H. S.: An Historical Survey of Psychosomatic Medicine. *J. Nerv. and Ment. Dis., 124*:546, 1956.
10. Harms, E.: The Early Historians of Psychiatry. *Am. J. Psychiat., 113*:749, 1957.
11. Sigerist, H. E.: Psychiatry in Europe at the Middle of the Nineteenth Century. In Hall, J. K. (Editor): *One Hundred Years of American Psychiatry.* New York, Columbia University Press, 1944.
12. Hunter, R. A. and Greenberg, H. P.: Sir William Gull and Psychiatry. *Guy's Hosp. Rep., 105*:361, 1956.
13. Mora, G.: Biagio Miraglia and the Development of Psychiatry in Naples in the Eighteenth and Nineteenth Centuries. *J. Hist. Med. & Allied Sc., 13*:504, 1958.
14. Mora, G.: Dramatic Presentations by Mental Patients in the Middle of the Nineteenth Century, and A. Dumas' Description. *Bull. Hist. Med., 31*:260, 1957.
15. Harms, E.: Modern Psychotherapy—150 Years Ago. *J. Ment. Sc., 103*:804, 1957.
16. Bromberg, W.: *Man Above Humanity.* Philadelphia, J. B. Lippincott, 1954.
17. Ackerknecht, E. H.: *A Short History of Medicine.* New York, Ronald Press, 1955.
18. Wall, J. H.: Problems in Schizophrenia. *N. Y. State J. Med., 56*:2864, 1956.
19. Winkler, J. K. and Bromberg, W.: *Mind Explorers.* New York, Reynal and Hitchcock, 1939.
20. Reik, L. E.: Short-term Hospital Treatment of Mental Illness: A Historical Perspective. *Ment. Hyg., 41*:74, 1957.
21. Deutsch, A.: *The Mentally Ill in America.* New York, Columbia University Press, 1946.
22. Overholser, W.: The Founding and Founders of the Association. In Hall, J. K.: *One Hundred Years of American Psychiatry.* New York, Columbia University Press, 1944.
23. Bond, E. D.: *Dr. Kirkbride and His Mental Hospital.* Philadelphia, J. B. Lippincott, 1947.
24. Carlson, E. T.: The Influence of Phrenology on Early American Psychiatric Thought. *Am. J. Psychiat., 115*:535, 1958.

25. Rond, P. C.: The First Professor of Psychiatry—Samuel Mitchell Smith. *Am. J. Psychiat., 114*:843, 1958.
26. Pollack, H. M.: Development of Statistics of Mental Disease in the United States During the Past Century. *Am. J. Psychiat., 102*:1, 1945.
27. Sanborn, F. B.: *Memoirs of Pliny Earle, M.D.* Boston, Damrell and Upham, 1898.
28. Klotter, A. S.: California Mental Hospitals. *Bull. Med. Lib. Assn., 45*:159, 1957.
29. Carlson, E. T.: Amariah Brigham: I. Life and Works. *Am. J. Psychiat., 112*:831, 1956.
30. Carlson, E. T.: Amariah Brigham: II. Psychiatric Thought and Practice. *Am. J. Psychiat., 113*:911, 1957.
31. Carlson, E. T.: Edward Mead and the Second American Psychiatric Journal. *Am. J. Psychiat., 113*:561, 1956.
32. Rond, P. C.: Ohio Psychiatric Pioneer—William Maclay Awl (1799-1876). *Ohio State M. J., 51*:882, 1955.
33. Stearns, A. W.: Isaac Ray, Psychiatrist and Pioneer in Forensic Psychiatry. *Am. J. Psychiat., 101*:573, 1945.
34. Pasamanick, B.: An Obscure Item in the Bibliography of Isaac Ray. *Am. J. Psychiat., 111*:164, 1954.
35. Diamond, B. L.: Isaac Ray and the Trial of Daniel M'Naughten. *Am. J. Psychiat., 112*:651, 1956.
36. Bett, W. R.: Isaac Ray (1807-81) of "Ray's Mania." *Med. Press, 237*:62, 1957.
37. Schneck, J. M.: A Note on Pliny Earle and Edgar Allan Poe. *Am. J. Psychiat., 116*:73, 1959.
38. Harms, E.: An Attempt to Formulate a System of Psychotherapy in 1818. *Am. J. Psychoth., 13*:269, 1959.

Courtesy of the New York Academy of Medicine

Chapter 10

THE NINETEENTH CENTURY (Concluded)

Dorothea Lynde Dix was a New England schoolteacher who developed an interest in the plight of the mentally ill. Her attack was on public indifference and her sights were directed toward legislative bodies. Her persistent activities spanned many years and her strivings for human betterment reaped returns (1). Her achievement has been called "a saga of raw courage and idealism" (4). Dorothea Dix is credited with playing an instrumental role in the founding or development of more than thirty state institutions for the mentally ill. The abuse and neglect of the indigent mentally sick attracted her attention in particular, and her searching curiosity and determination took her through almshouses and local jails where defective care and lack of attention emerged in bold view. With the dawn of some enlightenment, the sick were removed to small institutions functioning on a local community level. County hospitals were built and then replaced by larger state hospitals.

Henry has commented on the development of this phase of psychiatric care (2). There were then, and there still are problems and differences of opinion in this area. With the erection of large hospitals it was found that sizable numbers of patients could be maintained with greater economy. Often, this took precedence over the actual welfare of patients. As might be imagined, clashes were frequent between patient-minded physicians and economy-minded legislative bodies. The advantage of the larger hospitals pertained to greater uniformity and evaluation of treatment for those who favored such uniformity. Problems grew when physicians became increasingly absorbed with administrative duties, precluding adequate contact with the sick they were supposed to aid. The idea of a colonization arrangement was reconsidered, with its possible advantages, and the plan at Gheel was put forward as a fine example. As has been noted earlier, even Gheel had come in for criticism. The point, nevertheless, was to have private and public patients placed in cottages or homes, allowing for more extensive personal liberties. A small hospital would receive patients on admission prior to later placement throughout the village of homes and cottages. Patients, under this arrangement, would be visited by supervisors functioning under a physician-in-charge. Objections to such administration related to suicidal risks and improper treatment of patients because of insufficient control and scrutiny. This system of care for the mentally ill did find its place, nevertheless, in various parts of the United States and Canada, and a cottage system plan had been used with success in Scotland (2).

Well in the past, patients had been classified as curable and incurable. Gradually there was further refinement when divisions were created according to therapeutic needs. This developmental trend found expression eventually in the creation of Psychopathic Hospitals on an independent level of functioning. Also, there began to emerge the psychiatric wards within general hospitals. Henry mentions as the first Psychopathic Hospital, that in Heidelberg which appeared in 1878. In 1879 the one associated with Bellevue came on the scene and observation with temporary detention was stressed. Many others came into being subsequently. The point involved primarily for such institutions had to do with research study and treatment of early cases of mental disease. Interest in early treatment did not await the development of the separate psychopathic hospitals, however, for in 1751 there was stress at St. Luke's Hospital in England on treatment of patients ill for less than one year. Henry has pointed out also that the idea of psychiatric wards in general hospitals is not really new because historical antecedents are known. During the thirteenth century, a general hospital in Cairo offered such services, and in 1728, special wards of this type were on hand in Guy's Hospital, London. A similar plan existed in 1792 at the New York Hospital. The current trend under this plan favors careful observation with short-term, intensive treatment of acute personality disorders (2). Often the psychopathic hospitals have been connected with medical centers, thus furnishing opportunities not only for research, but for instruction of medical students in psychiatry. Rapid increase and development of mental health or psychiatric clinics connected with various hospitals has, of course, been a more recent occurrence.

During the first half of the nineteenth century there was focussing of attention in various ways on the problem of disturbed behavior with anti-social components. Not always, however, was there willingness to view such disturbance to be a reflection of mental illness, as evidenced by much of the reaction in objections to findings in the case of Daniel M'Naughten.

In 1835, J. C. Prichard (1786-1848) published *A Treatise on Insanity and Other Disorders Affecting the Mind.* He presented "moral insanity" as a particular type of illness (2). He divided insanity into four categories and they are believed to have stemmed from French psychiatric views. As for moral insanity, it was "madness, consisting in a morbid perversion of the natural feelings, affections, inclinations, temper, habits, moral dispositions, and natural impulses, without any remarkable disorder or defect of the intellect or knowing and reasoning faculties, and particularly without any insane delusion or hallucination" (3). Perversion of natural feelings has been translated to anti-social in current terminology. Many attempts have been made through the years to define this concept and different descriptive terms have been used. All the efforts in connection with this general issue of criminal behavior have implied considerable thought with constructive intent. English and American psychiatry has been singled out especially in connection with such endeavors (2). In any case, Prichard's views are believed to have had little influence in the setting of the M'Naughten trial for example (3). In another context, his ideas have been considered to reflect psychotherapy within the compass of moral treatment when he said, "to direct the attention of patients to the subjects on which their illusions turn, or to oppose their unreasonable prejudices by argument, or contradiction" is not indicated. "It is better," he affirmed, "to excite interest in connection with things remote from the morbid train of thought" (4).

Concern with anti-social behavior must bring to mind the work of Cesare Lombroso (1836-1909). He was an original thinker in the field of psychiatry and his studies were of broad scope (5). He was interested in anatomy, physiology, and psychology, and is regarded as the founder of Italian anthropology. Lombroso was the author of the books *Genius and Insanity,* issued in 1864, and *Delinquent Man,* published in 1876. Both works were widely read and translated. His studies of pellagra and cretinism played a role in their ultimate control within Italy. Lewis has affirmed that Lombroso's claims about special characteristics of criminal types have not been validated in studies since then, but his work in this field influenced directions of investigations in legal medicine (5). This applies also to the study of anthropology. Lombroso's students were men of influence, as in the case of Eugenio Morselli (1852-1929) who established the first laboratory of experimental psychiatry, and Leonardo Bianchi who furthered the teaching of psychiatry in Naples in 1890 and developed a neuropsychiatric clinic.

At this time there was ample evidence of continuing interest in classification. One major view emphasized categorizing on the basis of symptoms. Often this approach was favored because of serious questions about the accuracy of ideas concerning etiology. An example of this view is found in the work of David Skae published in 1863, *The Classification of the Various Forms of Insanity on a Rational and Practical Basis.* A mental disease grouping based on etiology is represented by the work of H. Maudsley (1835-1918) who published *The Physiology and Pathology of the Mind* in 1867. Zilboorg sees his system as typical for this period and of the type which appealed to the German psychiatrists. Under this classification, mental diseases were brain diseases, with special attention to anemia, toxicity, circulatory defects, and infection. These were causes of illness. The psychological counterparts were overwork or overexertion of bodily functions. The view has been expressed that in general the stress on classification was accompanied by decreased interest in the patient as an individual. Zilboorg feels, for example, that Maudsley, despite concern about environmental studies, had less feeling for the individual than did Tuke (2).

The history of psychiatry in Germany during the nineteenth century involved to a great extent a struggle between factions favoring stress on somatic aspects of mental illness and those favoring the importance of psychological aspects. Psychological views stemming from the romanticism of the early nineteenth century were not in favor with psychiatrists of an anatomico-physiological orientation. Somatological emphasis prevailed by mid-century (2).

The mid-century predominant view is associated strongly with Wilhelm Griesinger (1817-1868). As Ackerknecht has phrased it, with his work psychiatry passed into the hands of Germans (6). Griesinger had been a student of infectious diseases and discovered hookworm anemia. He involved himself in medical practice, physiological studies, and medical editing. In 1845, his book, *Pathologie und Therapie der Psychischen Krankheiten* was published. Its emphasis was on the relationships between psychological disorders and diseases of the nervous system. Lewis praises it as a remarkable book (5). It may be noted that he was only twenty-eight years old when it was issued. Earlier, he had spent two years studying at a mental hospital. Later, in 1866, he became chief of the psychiatric division at the Charité in Berlin and his direct contact with clinical psychiatry was reinstated. For Griesinger, psychological disease was brain disease. Since psychological reaction was considered a reflex reaction of the brain, it has been suggested that his ideas were forerunners of the concepts of Bechterew and Pavlov, and of twentieth century behaviorism. In line with some mental hospital trends of this period it should be noted that Griesinger too is credited with the introduction of non-restraint into mental hospitals (2). The over-all influence of psychiatric trends associated with Griesinger and others similarly inclined, was toward the employment of hydrotherapy, electrotherapy, and chemotherapy in a setting of improved hospital environments. Whether or not it was to be an exaggeration of fact as has been claimed, Theodor Ziehen, shortly before the turn of the twentieth century, was to describe psychology and psychotherapy as stepchildren of medicine (7).

Preferences for treatment methods, as indicated for Griesinger, have been given accurately nevertheless. Electrotherapy, in the form of galvanic and faradic currents, was widely used in psychiatry. Toward the close of the nineteenth century there was increasing doubt about its effectiveness, at least to the extent that might have been desired (8). Also, there was greater recognition of the psychological implications involved, despite limited understandings. The latter were integrated with the concept of suggestion as it was evaluated at that time with special reference to hysterical disorders.

A contemporary of Griesinger, Heinrich Neumann (1814-1884), saw human personality functioning as an integrated whole. The organism was intact as long as it functioned efficiently as a unit. Mental illness occurs when functions of the total personality operate no longer as a firm part of the unit. Neumann spoke of "recovery with defect" (2).

Alcoholism was of concern to many psychiatrists at this time. It was a clinical and public health issue in France, as it is today. Magnan studied it carefully. At the beginning of this period, near the turn of the century, Hufeland had presented the term "dipsomania." Magnus Huss referred to chronic alcoholism in mid-century. Wernicke described alcoholic hallucinosis (2). Delirium tremens was differentiated as a syndrome by Thomas Sutton in 1813 and toward the close of the century, in 1887, Korsakoff (1854-1900) became identified with his description of multiple neuritis, memory deficiency, disorientation, and confabulation (9). Henry has pointed out that in past centuries, delerium tremens had been described as a form of phrenitis. Sutton's contribution was called *Tracts On Delerium Tremens.* Korsakoff's psychosis was referred to as *cerebropathica psychia toxemia* (2). The study of morphine and other addictions, drugs of various types, and infections and poisons, became increasingly systematized by Karl Bonhoeffer. Mental disease was divided into exogenous and endogenous groups by Moebius (1853-1907), a division acceptable to Kraepelin (2).

Opinion has been rendered that somatologists with extreme views contributed to the feeling of therapeutic nihilism during this century. Attempts at therapy are believed by Zilboorg to have been influenced particularly by concepts of Brown relating to nervous system tonus with sthenic and asthenic states. Such influence is believed to be represented in the "neurasthenia" of George Miller Beard (1839-1883) and the "rest treatment" of Silas Weir Mitchell (1829-1914). John Brown of the Brunonian system has been described as an odd person combining qualities of naivete and unscrupulousness. According to him, life was based on stimulation from the brain and emotions on the one hand, and food and other external stimuli in addition. There were two categories of disease. The sthenic involved increased excitability and the asthenic, decreased excitability. Sedatives like laudanum, and stimulants of which whiskey was considered an example, were used to oppose the disease trends. The simplicity of these measures had wide appeal. His views have been claimed to be an oversimplification of those proposed by William Cullen (10). Cullen saw life maintained by brain energy extending from the central nervous system to muscles and solid organs. Muscles were a continuation of the medullary substance of the nervous system. A hypothetical fluid, not in fact a liquid, was the means of transmission of this energy to nerve endings. The energy maintained a state of excitement in the healthy. Lack of excitement resulted in disease (10). Cullen's views were clearly derived from concepts that had developed long before him. I believe it requires little imagination to see similarities in such views with current concepts of many sorts, including some aspects of libidinal processes in conventional psychoanalytic formulations.

Bromberg credits Beard with having centered attention on nervous exhaustion as a practical problem for neurologists instead of permitting it to rest only on a diagnostic level (1). To the extent that ideas inherent in it can be traced back at least to Brown and Cullen, it seems doubtful to me that its basic therapeutic aspects had ever really been ignored. It is true, nevertheless, that neurasthenia became a fashionable diagnosis. Bromberg has indicated that the symptom complex combined what would ordinarily be classified as hysteria, and symptoms involving autonomic nervous system dysfunction. E. H. Van Deusen has been cited as having antedated Beard in his description. Men of the calibre of Beard, Mitchell, and their associates, have been pointed up as significant in the development of American psychiatry, with special attention to the role of the practicing neurologist in this development. For Casamajor to claim that Beard was the first to introduce psychological medicine to America is, however, an unwarranted exaggeration (11). For some it might be considered more reasonable to refer to Mitchell, however, as the first American neurologist whether or not the gesture were accompanied by the tribute of saying that he was for some time also the leading psychiatrist in the United States (12). In any case, Mitchell has been cited with Thomas Salmon and Austen Riggs with reference to the basically important role of the personality of the therapist, when considering the very important question of training of psychotherapists to meet present day requirements (13).

One of the main associations with Mitchell is his Rest Cure. This involved rest, proper food, and isolation. Contact with relatives was prohibited and there resulted complete separation from the surroundings in which illness developed. This method of treating the patient gained wide popularity during the latter part of the nineteenth century. It overlapped the phase of electrotherapy associated in Europe with Wilhelm Erb.

A particular event in Mitchell's career that stands out in the history of American Psychiatry is his criticism of the profession administered in the course of an address in 1894 to the American Medico-Psychological Association on the occasion of its fiftieth anniversary. More recently, however, the claim has been voiced by Whitehorn that aside from any stimulus it may have served, taking the group to task on the scientific status of psychiatry did not properly reflect the level of scientific investigation at the time nor did it establish the main lines of future investigations. The several decades to follow witnessed work along psychological channels with emphasis on interpersonal relations rather than neurologically based research (14).

Mitchell has received a full measure of praise. He was an unusual man, a contributor to neurology, psychiatry and toxicology, author of poems, short stories, novels and biography. He is mentioned as the most versatile American since Benjamin Franklin (15). His writings have been studied carefully for their psychiatric insights and reflections of his clinical experience (16). Here again, the comment appears about anticipating Freud's findings (17). His biographer notes that Mitchell was "almost" a genius, adding that his contemporaries considered him such and that this opinion was one which Mitchell came to share (15).

In opposition to the concept of neurasthenia was the view of cerebral hyperaemia as proposed by William A. Hammond. He had gained distinction as a specialist in mental disease and disorders of the nervous system, and as Surgeon General of the United States Army during the Civil War. Although Hammond's ideas received some attention, they did not compete strongly with the neurasthenia concept (18).

The close of the nineteenth century saw the blossoming of descriptive psychiatry, but numerous stepping stones, important in themselves, led up to this development. Some may be singled out now. Carl Westphal (1833-1890), for example, was one of the earliest to describe obsessional states. He was interested also in homosexuality and in agoraphobia. He is linked with the idea of obsessional conditions as "abortive insanity," and his interests are related to the increasing trend in evaluating the neuroses, a trend exemplified further in the concerns of Krafft-Ebing and Pierre Janet (2). It is Janet who is remembered for the introduction of the diagnostic term "psychasthenia." Carl Wernicke (1848-1905) studied aphasia and noticed memory defects for recent periods with clear retention of events in the distant past, as revealed in some types of structural brain disorders.

Paranoia is said to be the first clinical picture to be revealed with great clarity in German psychiatric literature (2). William Sander (1838-1922) discussed it in 1868. Paranoid conditions had been discussed by others from several points of view before this. In the German setting, paranoia obtained a special place as a separate disease in systems of classification. Meynert and his co-workers were concerned with paranoid conditions. Theodore Meynert worked for many years in Vienna and his neuroanatomic studies have prompted Lewis to refer to him as "the father of the architectonics of the brain" (5). Keeping in mind the somatological emphasis of psychiatry in Germany, we may note at this point that Lewis cites Ernst Horn (1772-1848) as the first clinical psychiatrist in Germany to propose the view of mental disease as entirely physically determined. Similar views were advanced by Maximilian Jacobi (1775-1858). This trend is manifested further in the later, fruitful work of Franz Nissl (1860-1918) and Alois Alzheimer (1864-1915) involving studies of the nervous system in its microscopic structure. It was very difficult, however, to supply significant evidence of correlations between mental disorder and structural alterations of nerve cells (5). These difficulties persisted despite Alzheimer's observations in some dementia praecox patients, of reduction in number of ganglion cells and various evidences of cell degeneration. Alzheimer is especially associated with the disease that carries his name.

It is Korsakoff (1853-1900) who is often regarded as the first outstanding psychiatrist in Russia (5). He has already been mentioned in connection with alcoholism. In 1887, Korsakoff was placed in charge of the first psychiatric clinic in that country. His interests covered the range of psychiatric disorders and his research center attracted students of neuroanatomy and neuropathology from far and wide. At the same time he was evidently concerned with complete personality evaluations of patients. He was regarded as kind and sympathetic toward his patients, attitudes which are consistent with the role he is also credited with playing in the further advance of non-restraint in psychiatric care. He introduced it in Russia in 1881 at a private mental hospital in the face of adverse professional criticism, and he is quoted as saying that his procedures were not essentially the mechanical removal of physical restraint, but treatment involving greater attention and devotion to the needs of the patients. Korsakoff was apparently familiar with the work of William Tuke and John Conolly (19).

Elsewhere in Russia, V. M. Bechterew (1857-1928), a student of neurology, neurophysiology, and psychology, having worked with DuBois-Reymond, Wundt, Flechsig, and Charcot, formed a psychophysiological laboratory at Kazan University, developed mechanistic concepts which Lewis feels bear resemblances to Pavlov and Watson, and founded the Brain Institute in Leningrad (5). Boring considers him more of a psychiatrist than a physiologist. The Russian pioneer in reflexology was Ivan M. Sechenov (1825-1905), according to Boring, and Lewis has referred to him as the Father of Russian Physiology. Pavlov was his junior and read his work but did not receive direct instruction from him (20).

Prior to the Kraepelinian consolidations toward the close of the century, there were a number of related, important developments in clinical psychiatry. One, for example, was the description of catatonia associated especially with Karl Kahlbaum (1828-1899). His monograph of 1874 was *Die Katatonie odor das Spannungsirresein*. Kahlbaum was concerned with symptom complexes and he was free in acknowledging the obscure nature of the basis of mental disorder (5). He described the conditions of attitudinizing, posturing, and stuporous states in catatonia and introduced the term "verbigeration" in his monograph (2). He is credited with presenting also the above-mentioned expression, "symptom complex," and the term "cyclothymia." His friend, Ewald Hecker, wrote about hebephrenia in 1871 as a psychosis starting in puberty and moving toward rapid deterioration.

By 1896 Emil Kraepelin (1856-1926) was able to present dementia praecox as a group of several reaction patterns classified under this heading. The forms consisted of the simple, the hebephrenic, catatonic, and paranoid (21). The underlying defect was obscure but he considered the possibility of autointoxication in a setting of metabolic disturbance. Since it was felt that little could be done for it, the outlook was almost invariably pessimistic. The view is often expressed that Kraepelin, in his systematic fashion, eliminated much of the confusion in psychiatry at this time, but when he is referred to as the Father of Descriptive Psychiatry, the title is not always considered complimentary (22). This seems particularly true for psychiatrists today who, for some reason, find it difficult to reconcile the merits of Kraepelinian aptitudes and inclinations with ideas of dynamic psychiatry as implied in present day usage. For some, the development of psychiatric ideas as advanced by Kraepelin constituted a movement away from philosophical backgrounds and toward a scientific thinking linked with advances in clinical medicine (23). For them there was increasing comfort to the degree that such parallel developments could be achieved.

Kraepelin has been described as simple, shy, unsophisticated, and naive in certain ways. The latter characteristic would not be peculiar to him. It has been mentioned in connection with Freud, whose scientific contributions took so different a form. He was regarded as an impressive speaker, but not eloquent (24). Again, as has been said for others, he became a psychiatrist because it was a means toward earning his living. His true interest was perhaps closer to experimental psychology and little has been credited to him in the way of concern about therapy (25).

Kraepelin's organization of clinical data and psychiatric observations found expression in his famous textbook, *Psychiatrie, Ein Lehrbuch für Studierende und Aertze.* One commentator has voiced an opinion to the effect that reading the nine editions of this work is like reading the history of psychiatry (26). He worked over groupings of mental illness tirelessly. Proper classification was extremely important and he attended to this task with a critical eye. The degree to which he took pains in this connection has been felt to be inadequately appreciated (27).

In one of his publications, Zilboorg outlined some views he had expressed on more than one occasion having to do with Kraepelin, Bleuler and Freud. These views noted first that all three were contemporaries and long-lived. They completed the essentials of the tasks they had assumed. The work of each was not in opposition to the others. Kraepelin furthered astute clinical psychiatric observation, Bleuler presented pictures of ideational and affective content, and Freud illuminated this content. The work of these contributors developed simultaneously. The results were an outgrowth of trends in nineteenth century psychiatry (28).

Kraepelin was concerned with causes of mental illness, the beginnings, development, and outcome. He was always interested in the possible relationships between psychotic states and infectious diseases. His classification attempts were related to similar developments in the field of internal medicine. Focus of attention on pathology, diagnosis, and prognosis was consistent with concurrent general medicine parallels. Psychological systems were not a part of this outlook (5). There is frequent reference to the relative absence of contact that existed for Kraepelin as far as the inner psychological functions of the individual were concerned. This has been linked with his biological outlook and the view that biological method is directed essentially at the discovery of the laws pertaining to natural phenomena with stress on generalizations rather than individual variations (2).

The close link between diagnosis and prognosis stands out particularly in the Kraepelinian system and has influenced attitudes adopted toward it. If the prognosis had been correctly predicted, the diagnosis implied with it possessed concurrent validity. This was in line with the idea that certain types of illnesses had natural courses, and these courses were studied within the context of the mass of clinical data accumulated. It has been shown that for about forty years the concept of dementia praecox had undergone gradual development. It was synthesized by Kraepelin. His points of view were not accepted immediately, and conservative psychiatrists at that time were slow in agreeing to the new claims. Bleuler's influence is believed to have contributed to the attention given to Kraepelin's propositions (2). Kraepelin's division of psychoses into endogenous and exogenous categories followed Moebius. Dementia praecox was endogenous. The idea of a metabolic origin followed earlier assumptions of structural brain changes. The separate delineation of manic-depressive psychoses was not readily accepted by all concerned. Involutional melancholia was separated from other classifications and when it was strongly claimed by others to be part of the manic-depressive category, Kraepelin reversed his views, reluctantly or not. In historical perspective it should not be difficult, I believe, to accept the fact that these diagnostic linkages and separations proved difficult and troublesome repeatedly. The problems along these lines that arise constantly in every-day clinical experience should be sufficient to attest to the complexities so often encountered, to differences in opinion and points of view in any particular time period by admittedly experienced clinicians, and to the obvious artificiality of so many diagnostic constructions no matter how legitimately important they may be for immediate, practical purposes.

Earlier, I used the expression, Kraepelinian consolidation. The idea, however, that Kraepelin established a psychiatric era in itself has been questioned on the ground that it emerged from historical steps in a way that can be traced, and with gradual transition (2).

At this time, while much attention was given to the study of dementia praecox, there was continued effort to understand the problem of syphilitic infection and its relation to general paralysis. Experimental work of Krafft-Ebing demonstrated that patients with this illness did not respond with evidences of syphilitic infection on inoculation, the interpretation being that they could not do so because they were already infected and general paralysis was indeed a manifestation of results of such original infection. The experimental findings were stated in 1897. General paralysis, it should be recalled, had been observed for some time, and considered by many to be a manifestation of mental disease. In line with this, as Henry has pointed out, tabes dorsalis was seen by some authors in the nineteenth century as general paralysis without mental derangement (2). Scipion Pinel was one of many who linked general paresis to alcoholic and sexual overindulgence, but in 1857 Esmarch and Jessen proposed syphilis as the essential cause (2). The latter interpretation did not meet with ready acceptance, and one of the outstanding examples of the opposition was Griesinger. T. S. Clouston is credited as the first to focus attention on juvenile paresis. This was in 1877. Alzheimer supplied extensive histopathologic descriptions of general paresis in 1904. In that year, Kraepelin was able to say that syphilitic infection must antedate the later appearance of paresis.

Dealing here with issues involving much emphasis on structural pathology, it may be pertinent to highlight a point of interest in the objection of Meynert, one of Freud's teachers, to the term "psychiatry." The objection was based on its inconsistency with the view of an essentially somatic basis of mental illness (29). This is in contrast to the thinking of men who came earlier, and as far as the nineteenth century is concerned, Johann Christian Heinroth (1773-1843) may be mentioned in this connection because of his awareness of the essential importance of psychological processes for an evaluation of total personality functioning. Reference may be made also to Alexander Haindorf (1782-1862), author of the first German textbook on mental disease (2). He is believed to have approached the significance of psychological conflict in the expression of psychological illness.

Certain psychological manifestations in elderly people had been observed for some time. Felix Plater had noticed the interference with memory in older people with particular reference to recent events. Senile dementia had been studied by Esquirol. Not only memory changes, but narrowing of attention span, uncertainty of the "will," a tendency toward sensitiveness in reaction to minor issues, and excitable behavior, had been commented on. With individuals showing some of the aforementioned characteristics and mental confusion, amnesic phenomena, and related characteristics, Redlich in 1898 noted brain changes involving miliary plaques with senile cerebral atrophy (2).

Hand in hand with emphasis on the structural and descriptive, came attention by some to psychological forces at play in personality functioning and stress on attempting to view what lay beneath the surface in the psychological life of the individual. Friedrich Gross, a student of Nasse is an example of this trend (2). In addition it will be remembered that Langermann had been a teacher of Ideler. The feasibility of a psychological theory of mental illness was favored by Ideler who served as chief of the Berlin Charité. He died in 1860 and his ideas were almost forgotten for a time. The psychobiological, sociological, and anthropological influences in medical psychology were of concern to him.

The physician, Carl Gustav Carus (1789-1869) was interested in physiognomy. He was concerned with unconscious mental life and his *Psyche* (1846) is concerned with it. Carus is known for his long friendship with Goethe (30, 31). Carus wrote: "Progressively, consciousness arises and develops itself, but conscious life remains always under the influence of the unconscious, and in sleep the individual periodically returns to it."

Eduard von Hartmann published in 1869 his *Philosophy of the Unconscious* which has been included among the speculative thinking and claims of the German romantic philosophy of this century (30). He proposed three layers of the unconscious. The first was a pervasive absolute unconscious. The second, a physiological unconscious. The third, a relative or psychological unconscious from which conscious mental life derives. Boring has pointed out of Lotze that, for him, the brain was the organ of consciousness, and action within the cord must be unconscious (20). This may serve as a link to the aforementioned designation of a physiological unconscious.

At present there are attempts to link findings and theory based on psychoanalytic psychology with techniques and observations in the realm of a more traditional experimental psychology. Among the founders of the latter are Fechner, Wundt who was a teacher of Kraepelin, and the physician-scientist Hermann von Helmholtz (1821-1894). While Boring grants him this status, he points out that Helmholtz "held no brief" for the foundation of psychology as a science in its own right. It was only until after 1860, incidentally, that some scientists began to call themselves psychologists (20). Wundt was, of course, of great stature, and in America, William James (1842-1910), psychologist and philosopher, trained as a physician, may at times be compared to him by some (32). In view of Kraepelin's acknowledged ability to put together what was important in much that came before him and that had been observed by others, it is of interest to hear Murphy say of his teacher Wundt, that he attempted to bring together experimental psychology, child psychology, animal psychology, and folk psychology. He favored psychology as an independent science, may be called the Founder of Experimental Psychology, and, again according to Boring, we find Kraepelin rated as distinguished as any of Wundt's pupils (20).

In bringing to a close some of the highlights of nineteenth century problems and developments, and before the transitions into the twentieth century are discussed, it would be fitting to glance at the over-all picture of this period. To find psychiatric opinions on the period would be simple enough, but it is of greater interest perhaps to turn to an outstanding figure in one of the other medical specialties. In 1901, looking back on "Medicine in the Nineteenth Century" during an address to the Johns Hopkins Historical Club, William Osler said, "One of the most remarkable and beneficial reforms of the nineteenth century has been in the attitude of the profession and the public to the subject of insanity, and the gradual formation of a body of men in the profession who labour to find out the cause and means of relief of this most distressing of all human maladies. The reform movement inaugurated by Tuke in England, by Rush in the United States, by Pinel and Esquirol in France, and by Jacobi and Hasse in Germany, has spread to all civilized countries, and has led not only to an amelioration and improvement in the care of the insane, but to a scientific study of the subject which has already been productive of much good" (33).

REFERENCES

1. Deutsch, A.: *The Mentally Ill in America.* New York, Columbia University Press, 1946.
2. Zilboorg, G. and Henry, G. W.: *A History of Medical Psychology.* New York, W. W. Norton, 1941.
3. Leigh, D.: James Cowles Prichard, M.D., 1786-1848. *Proc. Royal Soc. Med., 48*:586, 1955.

4. Bromberg, W.: *Man Above Humanity.* Philadelphia, J. B. Lippincott, 1954.
5. Lewis, N. D. C.: *A Short History of Psychiatric Achievement.* London, Chapman and Hall, 1942.
6. Ackerknecht, E. H.: *A Short History of Medicine.* New York, Ronald Press, 1955.
7. Veith, I.: Freud's Place in the History of Medicine. *Behavioral Sc., 2*:67, 1957.
8. Stainbrook, E.: The Use of Electricity in Psychiatric Treatment During the Nineteenth Century. *Bull. Hist. Med., 22*:156, 1948.
9. Myerson, D. J.: The Study and Treatment of Alcoholism. A Historical Perspective. *New England. J. Med., 257*:820, 1957.
10. Johnstone, R. W.: William Cullen. *Med. Hist., 3*:33, 1959.
11. Casamajor, L.: Notes for an Intimate History of Neurology and Psychiatry in America. *J. Nerv. and Ment. Dis., 98*:600, 1943.
12. Penfield, W.: The Aegean Cradle of Medicine. *Trans. and Studies of the Coll. Phys. Phila., 24*:20, 1956.
13. Gildea, M. C. -L and Gildea, E. F.: Personalities of American Psychotherapists, Mitchell, Salmon, Riggs. *Am. J. Psychiat., 101*:460, 1945.
14. Whitehorn, J. C.: A Century of Psychiatric Research in America. In Hall, J. K.: *One Hundred Years of American Psychiatry.* New York, Columbia University Press, 1944.
15. Earnest, E.: *S. Weir Mitchell.* Philadelphia, University of Pennsylvania Press, 1950.
16. Rein, D. M.: *S. Weir Mitchell as a Psychiatric Novelist.* New York, International Universities Press, 1952.
17. Marti-Ibáñez, F.: Minerva and Aesculapius, The Physician as Writer. *Int. Rec. Med. and Gen. Pract. Clin., 169*:723, 1956.
18. Stearns, A. W.: A History of the Development of the Concept of Functional Nervous Disease During the Past Twenty-five Hundred Years. *Am. J. Psychiat., 103*:289, 1946.
19. Raskin, N.: Non-Restraint. *Am. J. Psychiat., 115*:471, 1958.
20. Boring, E. G.: *A History of Experimental Psychology.* New York, Appleton-Century-Crofts, 1950.
21. Wall, J. H.: Problems in Schizophrenia. *N. Y. State J. Med., 56*:2864, 1956.
22. Braceland, F. J.: Kraepelin, His System and His Influence. *Am. J. Psychiat., 113*:871, 1956.
23. Marti-Ibáñez, F., Sackler, A. M., Sackler, M. D. and Sackler, R. R.:

The Quest for Freud. *J. Clin. Exper. Psychopath., 17*:117, 1956.
24. Kahn, E.: Emil Kraepelin. *Am. J. Psychiat., 113*:289, 1956.
25. Krapf, E. E.: Response to Fellowship Lecture on Eugen Bleuler. *Am. J. Psychiat., 114*:299, 1957.
26. Mayer, W.: Emil Kraepelin (1856-1926). *Am. J. Psychoth., 10*:273, 1956.
27. Kahn, E.: A Marginal Note on Interpretation. *Am. J. Psychiat., 112*:393, 1955.
28. Zilboorg, G.: The Problem of Ambulatory Schizophrenia. *Am. J. Psychiat., 113*:519, 1956.
29. Reik, L. E.: The Historical Foundations of Psychotherapy in Schizophrenia. *Am. J. Psychoth., 10*:241, 1956.
30. Ellenberger, H.: The Unconscious Before Freud. *Bull. Menninger Clin., 21*:3, 1957.
31. Magnus, R.: *Goethe as a Scientist.* New York, Henry Schuman, 1949.
32. Roback, A. A.: *History of American Psychology.* New York, Library Publishers, 1952.
33. Osler, W.: *Aequanimitas.* Philadelphia, P. Blakiston's Son, 1932.

Courtesy of the New York Academy of Medicine

SIGMUND FREUD

Chapter 11

THE TWENTIETH CENTURY

We are in a position to look back on the first half of the present century. All of it is now a part of history but it is doubtful that we can be secure in our historical perspectives. Many of the events are much too close to permit accurate appraisals. Some apparently important developments have seen only initial stages and have yet to bear fruit or to show their true worth. A few highlights, especially in the very early decades, have achieved at least a measure of general acceptance that insures them a likely place in the future as far as recorded history is concerned. These views and the qualifications set on the circumstances of the more recent years must be kept in mind as we follow the additional threads of past events.

The work of several outstanding figures spanned the end of the nineteenth century and the beginning of the twentieth. One example is Ivan Pavlov (1849-1936) who, in his early years, moved in the direction of the priesthood and became diverted later toward medicine and physiology. As psychologist Robert S. Woodworth has put it, "By 1890 he had definitely 'arrived' as a leading physiologist" (1). A very productive scientist, Pavlov's extensive work on the physiology of the cardiovascular, digestive, and central nervous systems has been detailed in a meticulous biography (2). As is true of Freud and other unusual contributors, Pavlov has been discussed in voluminous writings from many points of view and with concern about numerous fine details in his thinking and activities (3).

Pavlov's neurophysiological interests led to investigations of the pancreatic nerves, discovery of the cardiac nerves, and exploration of the nerves associated with the digestive tract. Probably the main association to any mention of his contributions is the conditioned reflex. Pavlov was about fifty-five years old when the absorption with studies on conditioning got under way (4). He had already been awarded the Nobel prize for previous endeavors. Pavlov appears not to have been concerned basically with the issue of psychological ideas in his focus on the central nervous system. He was involved with observation of unconditioned reflexes and their role in the production of more complex, conditioned reactions as external factors were introduced. The researches as they influenced others resulted to a considerable extent in the bypassing of problems of consciousness and in the stimulation of a variety of studies on other aspects of psychological functioning. Yet the major impact in the United States was on work in the field of psychology rather than psychiatry specifically, and the special area it generally calls to mind is that of behaviorism. As for psychiatry, perhaps the greatest influence of Pavlovian thought has been in Russia. The extent to which this is true may become more evident at a later date. It would seem that Pavlov's doctrines have not generally played a role in the larger area of psychiatric practice and investigation as a unified, organized body of thought and in systematized application, but reference to, and utilization of his concepts certainly appear frequently in many publications. There are some laboratories in the United States that are grounded in his work. Lewis has noted a pertinent observation by one of Pavlov's students. "His contribution to science will probably not be so much what he has told us concerning the part played by excitation and inhibition and their spread and concentration as the fact that he has been the first to show definitely that the so-called psychical functions can be reduced to a method of quantitative measurements" (5).

Toward the close of the last century, the attack on the ravages of syphilitic involvement of the central nervous system began to bear fruit in areas of understanding, followed by treatment. In 1905, Schaudinn discovered the spirochaeta pallida in primary lesions and related them to the etiology of syphilis. In 1913, Hideyo Noguchi (1876-1928) and Moore demonstrated the organism in paretic brains (47). The last was the culmination of a long series of developments in the study of the disease with its many ramifications and obscurities. While in recent years there has been much focus on the antibiotics with special reference to penicillin, stemming from the observations in 1929 by Sir Alexander Fleming, the basic work and development of chemotherapy calls up the name of Paul Ehrlich (1854-1915), intimately related to the beginnings of this area in science (6). As for chemotherapy itself, Ackerknecht has termed it "one of the most significant medical achievements of the present century" (7). In 1910, Ehrlich developed salvarsan which revolutionized antiluetic therapy (8). He was assisted in this by Hata and the designation "606" heard often in reference to it, pertains to the 606th chemical combination that finally proved helpful in the form of arsphenamine. The chemotherapeutic achievement had, of course, been preceded by earlier treatment efforts along these lines, with mercury and iodides playing a long term role. Salvarsan was followed by neoarsphenamine for reduction in toxicity and the chain of additional developments continued.

In 1917, Wagner-Jauregg (1857-1940) of Vienna introduced malarial therapy for general paresis. He had been at work on this problem for several decades. Ten years later he received the Nobel Prize in physiology and medicine and was the first psychiatrist to be honored in this way (9). It had long been known that at times there would be remissions in psychotic reactions when intercurrent infectious diseases appeared. Wagner-Jauregg apparently considered the deliberate utilization of malaria for this purpose as far back as 1887 but had to wait thirty years to bring the idea to fruition (8). He experimented during the interval with tuberculin and typhoid vaccine. It is of interest to note that when it has been said of him that he approached psychiatry from the viewpoint of the biologist, it was claimed too that his work adhered to the principle of Wilhelm Griesinger proclaiming mental diseases to be diseases of the brain. This orientation is further elaborated with the observation that principles of dynamic psychiatry were alien to him (10).

Wagner-Jauregg prepared in 1935 a history of malarial therapy for general paralysis, and it has been made available relatively recently (11). An excerpt of historical interest reads, "In the literature Rosenblum is usually credited with being the first who inoculated general paralytics for therapeutic purposes, using recurrent fever and not malaria. The facts, however, are that Rosenblum has never inoculated his patients with the idea of treating their mental illness. What he did was to make available his mental patients—

among whom were no general paralytics—to the bacteriologist Motschutkoffsky, who in Odessa in the year of 1876 studied the transmissibility of recurrent fever to human beings. Subsequently, a few of these patients recovered from their psychoses and Rosenblum reported this later under an assumed name. Rosenblum never continued these experiments. The suggestion to treat mental cases with malaria was really made by Raggi in 1876 but he never put this idea into practice."

While this work was in progress, inroads were being effected into an understanding of one of the most important problems in mental disease. Here, attention is centered on Eugen Bleuler (1857-1939) whose renown is generally accepted in relation to his studies on schizophrenia and the psychopathology of the reactions classified under this heading. In 1898, Bleuler was appointed Professor of Psychiatry and Director of the Burghölzei (12). From the turn of the century, he was interested in the ideas of Freud and Abraham and in the growth of psychoanalysis (4). It should be added, however, that he is often regarded as having been ambivalent toward psychoanalysis. He was an original thinker, and it is worth remarking that it was Bleuler who centered attention, in his concerns, on the very issue of ambivalence, as well as on autistic thinking and the schizoid personality. Bleuler introduced the term "schizophrenia" with its alterations in thinking processes and disharmony of affect (13). With the patients' withdrawal, their ideas of reference, delusions and hallucinations were regarded as secondary reactions interpreted as efforts at adjustment in response to primary pathology. The psychogenesis of the secondary symptoms is regarded at times as the fundamentally important concept in his contribution (14). Undoubtedly it is not necessary to single out any one of the new views presented as representative for Bleuler in this respect.

Bleuler's major work published in 1911 was *Dementia Praecox odor die Gruppe der Schizophrenien.* Put forward by Bleuler were the ideas of a group of reactions rather than one specific disease entity, doubt about absence of affect in these reactions, and a questioning of the claim of incurability. His concept of dereistic thinking has been linked with Freud's observations of narcissistic reactions (8). Although Bleuler's views found general acceptance in the United States, it has been noted as curious that it was more than thirty years later when his book was finally translated into English. Long before this, however, he had presented his ideas about autistic thinking when invited by Adolf Meyer to visit the United States. Despite such strong stress on the psychological components of schizophrenia, Bleuler saw schizophrenia as an "organic" disease. This point has been delineated by Zilboorg when he comments too that Adolf Meyer thought of schizophrenia as "psychological" in origin. But as this is mentioned now I can only stress the remarkable confusion that arises because of semantic misunderstanding and lack of clarity. It reaches a point where, indeed, the likelihood of mutual misunderstanding is pronounced, impairing opportunities to view all disease from a more holistic vantage point. The basic issue of what is meant by what is said, will soon have to be taken into more serious consideration than it has to date. As a final note on Bleuler it may be mentioned that his opposition to stress on diagnostic labels in clinical, forensic, and social psychiatry has been regarded by some as one of his important attributes (15).

References have already been made to an early tie between the work of Janet and Freud, but it is worth reemphasizing that there has been a difference of opinion regarding the influence of Janet's contributions on Freud's formulations. By this time, claims of any real influence have been dampened considerably although Janet's individual efforts should certainly not be belittled. He continues to have strong supporters (16). His studies on hysteria and observations on dissociation will always have an historical niche. In this connection Henry A. Murray, for example, acknowledges his work as classic in its role of opening the channels to unknown areas of mental functioning (17). In line with, and as extensions of these interests and investigations was the work of Morton Prince (1854-1929) in America. He contributed to the elucidation of processes labeled as co-conscious, thoroughly examined certain manifestations of hysteria, studied hallucinations, and offered remarkable descriptions and observations of multiple personalities. It is usually agreed that he did not grasp or accept the implications of the unconscious in the Freudian meaning, and the opinion has been ventured that in his views of the unconscious he was influenced more by concepts such as those of von Hartmann (4). Prince's views were beyond those advanced by Charcot and, nearer to home, he had the stimulating influence of William James (18). In 1905, he published *The Dissociation of a Personality* "which created a sensation" (17). With the publication in 1914 of *The Unconscious* dealing with his extensive research, his reputation, according to Murray, was perhaps that of the most outstanding experimental psychiatrist. It is true, most likely, that his efforts should be seen in their importance for advancing at that time the theme of psychogenesis of many disorders, when strong emphasis in the medical profession centered on somatology. Prince is regarded as a "psychical monist" and a proponent of purposive psychology. His contributions, when finally registering impact, were soon overshadowed by the rapid development of psychoanalysis. Hypnotic techniques played an important role in his investigations and he holds a secure place in the historical development of these applications. Prince was the founder of the *Journal of Abnormal Psychology,* of the American Psychopathological Association, and of the Harvard Psychological Clinic.

The culmination in most understandings about the depths of mental functioning, insofar as present day knowledge is concerned, was reached in the Freudian crystallization of a dynamic unconscious. The main features have been summarized often in its description as the basis of active, primitive impulses with infantile, aggressive and sexual drives. The pleasure principle is pursued, time, death, logic, values, and morals are ignored. Unconscious elements find representation in dreams, symbols, parapraxes, neurotic symptoms, and symptomatic behavior. As Ellenberger has said, the map of a new continent was drawn, the unconscious was integrated into psychiatry, and it became a powerful battlefield for the psychotherapist (19). Attempts are made directly and by implication to set others up as equals of Freud, but at least from the view of current perspectives this is probably not reasonable. It has been said, for example, that the two great dynamists in psychology were Freud and William McDougall, and that McDougall was a dynamist before Freud gained a reputation beyond his small circle in Vienna, but such views do not at all diminish his stature (20). It is difficult to assess the significance of Freud's work briefly and adequately. Serious attempts to achieve this generally appear in writings other than the basically historical. It may be said, however, that his studies were of unusual depth and range. With numerous theoretical and clinical presentations he described the functioning of a dynamic unconscious in its numerous and complex manifestations. He developed the technique of psychoanalysis with its promise for assisting patients in overcoming their psychological difficulties. His psychological insights brought new perspectives to the fields of sociology, anthropology, literature, and history among others, transcending any immediate applications to psychology and psychiatry.

At the turn of the century Freud published *The Interpretation of Dreams,* an acknowledged classic. Within the next few years there appeared the *Psychopathology of Everyday Life* and *Three Contributions to the Theory of Sex.* His prolific writings have appeared in collections of one form or another and they run into series of many volumes.

In the second decade of this century, major cleavages in the early psychoanalytic circle appeared, the best known being the defections of Adler and Jung. Separations and new directions continued in the years thereafter. In 1909 Freud visited the United States to deliver the *Introductory Lectures on Psychoanalysis.* The invitation was extended by G. Stanley Hall (1846-1924), founder of the first American psychological journal and first president of the American Psychological Association (21). The acceptance and utilization of psychoanalytic concepts have apparently been greater in the United States than in the countries of Europe, a seeming paradox which is not unusual in many areas of science where at least initial recognition of contributors and their work is achieved in foreign lands rather than at home.

Because Freud's classic work on dreams was published at the turn of the century, and about forty of roughly fifty years of his independent scientific activities are part of this century, he has been regarded as basically a twentieth century figure (22). His early work with hypnosis was related more to nineteenth century endeavors as is evident in an evaluation of present day contributions many of which are dependent on formulations which Freud developed in the psychoanalytic field some time after he relinquished the use of hypnotic methods. It has been said of him that his reluctance to employ hypnosis for therapeutic purposes may have been a reaction formation in connection with his own fantasies of omnipotence (23). Regardless of the possible accuracy of this and other evaluations of Freud as a person, his major work clearly stands on its own merit in historical perspective.

A comparison between Freud and Charcot was described not long ago in an interesting way. It was essentially to the effect that Charcot saw neuroses whereas Freud heard them. Charcot dramatized neuroses whereas Freud employed auscultation of patients' verbalizations with the same concern as Laennec who listened to the chest sounds of those under his care (24).

Several times it has been mentioned that one or another contributor to the history of psychiatry has been declared a precursor of Freud. The repetition becomes tiresome, but lately at least one biographer of a noted medical figure, in this case Oliver Wendell Holmes, has been willing to call this judgment extravagant (25). It may be remembered that Holmes wrote a series of so-called psychiatric novels which received the careful scrutiny of the distinguished psychiatrist, Clarence P. Oberndorf, author also of a history of psychoanalysis in America (26, 27, 48).

As for comparisons of Freud with other men of great achievement, some have been alluded to already. Invariably named are Charles Darwin and Copernicus. It may be noted parenthetically that Darwin studied medicine for a brief period, and the biographer of Copernicus tells us it may be difficult to realize that during his lifetime Copernicus was thought of more highly and was perhaps known better as a physician than as an astronomer (28, 29). Freud has been put in the company of Newton, and he has been linked with Harvey (30). More recently, with strong support, he is given a place beside Parcelsus (31, 32).

Beyond these comparisons of spirit, personality, or significance of scientific achievement, Freud in connection with his own thought and efforts acknowledged the direct or indirect influence of others before him. He made reference, for example, to Fechner when he published his autobiography (33). Gustav Theodor Fechner (1801-1887) appears to have been of special influence in relation to the theoretical aspects of psychoanalysis. Specifically, the influence is seen to have played on the idea of mental energy, the topographical concept, and the principles of pleasure-unpleasure, constancy, and repetition. Ellenberger expresses the opinion that Fechner's concepts were geared to speculation "for its own sake" whereas Freud presented his concepts when they were required as tools in his work (34). Not long before he died, Freud began to write his outline of psychoanalysis. Although it was never finished, what was said is of interest and it constituted an attempt to bring together the basic tenets of psychoanalysis in concise and positive terms (35).

Since his death there have been a remarkable number of publications touching on every phase of Freud's thinking and feeling and clinical activities. Interest has been centered on his personal life, directly or indirectly (36). His case studies have been examined minutely, a particular favorite being the Schreber case (37). His works have been listed and re-listed (38). Personal accounts of training and analysis with him have been submitted (39). Controversial biographies have been written (40). Ernest Jones' three volume study of Freud is monumental in scope though surely not objective, and it will probably be unmatched for some time to come (41).

Writing of Freud's genius, Jones said elsewhere that it led to viewing mankind in a new way "although what he actually discovered was not in itself so very new." Furthermore, the "fearless and pioneering exploration" of these discoveries stood out prominently (42). Karl Menninger has referred to the discoveries as "revolutionary and world-shaking." He chooses to highlight Freud's character as his most lasting influence, however, with special reference to his persistence in the search for hidden data, his conviction of the lawfulness of psychic phenomena, his belief in the curability of the neuroses, his humility, courage, and patience (43).

Freud modified his formulations during the course of his

career. Others have suggested new points of view. There have been controversies over issues of theory and technique. Changes have been suggested because of unpredictability of results and discrepancies between the apparent helpfulness of psychoanalytic procedure and the length of treatment time as well as its intensity (44). Also, it had been fashionable to discredit therapeutic change with other procedures, especially short-term methods, as transference cures. More recently the stability of such changes in certain cases and the subsequent meaningful personality alterations have been acknowledged by at least some therapists trained in the psychoanalytic tradition although they had long been observed and claimed by others (45). Apparently, modifications in technique are more prevalent than the psychiatric literature alone would indicate, and the practice of what is often called classical psychoanalysis occurs to a lesser extent than is ordinarily believed (46).

By mid-century many differences of opinion in connection with theory and method had developed and the broad field of psychoanalysis experienced a variety of cleavages with the establishment of several separate groups functioning largely as self-contained units. Certain premises are shared in common, but the differences are frequently highlighted. While these cleavages have developed on the one hand, there has been on the other a gradually increasing integration of the basic principles of psychoanalytic thought into the over-all practice and development of psychiatry as a medical specialty, and to the extent that this has been accomplished, with the relinquishing of special allegiances, gains have been achieved for psychiatry as a scientific discipline.

REFERENCES

1. Woodworth, R. S.: *Contemporary Schools of Psychology.* New York, Ronald Press, 1948.
2. Babkin, B. P.: *Pavlov, A Biography.* Chicago, University of Chicago Press, 1949.
3. Razran, G.: Pavlov and Lamarck. *Science, 128*:758, 1958.
4. Lewis, N. D. C.: *A Short History of Psychiatric Achievement.* London, Chapman and Hall, 1942.

5. Gantt, W. H.: *Russian Medicine.* New York, Paul B. Hoeber, 1937.
6. Marquardt, M.: *Paul Ehrlich.* New York, Henry Schuman, 1951.
7. Ackerknecht, E. H.: A Short History of Medicine. New York, Ronald Press, 1955.
8. Zilboorg, H. and Henry, G. W.: *A History of Medical Psychology.* New York, W. W. Norton, 1941.
9. Dattner, B.: Julius Wagner von Jauregg (1857-1940). In Haymaker, W.: *The Founders of Neurology.* Springfield, Thomas, 1953.
10. Silbermann, M.: Julius Wagner von Jauregg. *Am. J. Psychiat., 113*:1057, 1957.
11. Wagner-Jauregg, J.: The History of the Malaria Treatment of General Paralysis (Comment and Translation from the German by Walter L. Bruetsch). *Am. J. Psychiat., 102*:577, 1946.
12. Krapf, E. E.: Response to Fellowship Lecture on Eugen Bleuler. *Am. J. Psychiat., 114*:299, 1957.
13. Wall, J. H.: Problems in Schizophrenia. *N. Y. State J. Med., 56*:2864, 1956.
14. Reik, L. E.: The Historical Foundations of Psychotherapy in Schizophrenia. *Am. J. Psychoth., 10*:241, 1956.
15. Zilboorg, G.: Eugen Bleuler and Present-Day Psychiatry. *Am. J. Psychiat., 114*:289, 1957.
16. Bailey, P.: Janet and Freud. *A. M. A. Arch. Neurol. and Psychiat., 76*:76, 1956.
17. Murray, H. A.: Morton Prince: Sketch of His Life and Work. *J. Abn. and Soc. Psychol., 52*:291, 1956.
18. Morris, L.: *William James.* New York, Charles Scribner's Sons, 1950.
19. Ellenberger, H.: The Unconscious Before Freud. *Bull. Menninger Clin., 21*:3, 1957.
20. Roback, A. A.: *History of American Psychology.* New York, Library Publishers, 1952.
21. Sargent, S. S.: *The Basic Teachings of the Great Psychologists.* Philadelphia, Blakiston Company, 1944.
22. Zilboorg, G.: *Sigmund Freud.* New York, Charles Scribner's Sons, 1951.
23. Ehrenwald, J.: History of Psychoanalysis. In: *Science and Psychoanalysis.* New York, Grune and Stratton, 1958.
24. Marti-Ibáñez, F.: The Historical and Philosophic Background of

Psychobiology. *J. Clin. Exper. Psychopath., 17*:360, 1956.
25. Tilton, E. M.: *Amiable Autocrat, A Biography of Dr. Oliver Wendell Holmes.* New York, Henry Schuman, 1947.
26. Oberndorf, C. P.: *The Psychiatric Novels of Oliver Wendell Holmes.* New York, Columbia University Press, 1945.
27. Oberndorf, C. P.: *A History of Psychoanalysis in America.* New York, Grune and Stratton, 1953.
28. Sears, P. B.: *Charles Darwin.* New York, Charles Scribner's Sons, 1950.
29. Armitage, A.: *Sun, Stand Thou Still.* New York, Henry Schuman, 1947.
30. Macalpine, I.: Tribute to Freud. *J. Hist. Med. & Allied Sc., 11*:247, 1956.
31. Galdston, I.: Freud and Romantic Medicine. *Bull. Hist. Med., 30*:489, 1956.
32. Zilboorg, G.: Freud's One Hundredth Anniversary. *Psychoanal. Quart., 25*:139, 1956.
33. Freud, S.: *An Autobiographical Study.* New York, W. W. Norton, 1952.
34. Ellenberger, H. F.: Fechner and Freud. *Bull. Menninger Clin., 20*:201, 1956.
35. Freud, S.: *An Outline of Psychoanalysis.* New York, W. W. Norton, 1949.
36. Schneck, J. M.: A Note on Freud's Neighbor. *Am. J. Psychoth., 13*:139, 1959.
37. Macalpine, I. and Hunter, R. A.: The Schreber Case. *Psychoanal. Quart., 22*:328, 1953.
38. Tyson, A. and Strachey, J.: A Chronological Hand-List of Freud's Works. *Int. J. Psycho-Analysis,* 37:19, 1956.
39. Wortis, J.: *Fragments of an Analysis with Freud.* New York, Simon and Schuster, 1954.
40. Puner, H. W.: *Freud, His Life and His Mind.* New York, Grosset and Dunlap, 1947.
41. Jones, E.: *The Life and Work of Sigmund Freud.* New York, Basic Books, 1953-57.
42. Jones, E.: Nature of Genius. *Sc. Monthly, 84*:75, 1957.
43. Menninger, K.: Sigmund Freud. *Menninger Quart., 10*:5, 1956.
44. Alexander, F. and French, T. M.: *Psychoanalytic Therapy.* New York, Ronald Press, 1946.
45. Alexander, F.: Discussion of Paul H. Hoch: Aims and Limita-

tions of Psychotherapy. *Am. J. Psychiat., 112*:321, 1955.
46. Knight, R. P.: The Present Status of Organized Psychoanalysis in the United States. *J. Am. Psychoanal. Assn., 1*:197, 1953.
47. Eckstein, G.: Noguchi. New York, Harper & Brothers, 1931.
48. Schneck, J. M.: Oliver Wendell Holmes. *Am. J. Surg., 71*:560, 1946.

Chapter 12

THE TWENTIETH CENTURY (Continued)

Carl Gustav Jung (1875-) was born in Switzerland and was graduated from the University of Basel. He studied at the Burghölzli in Zurich when Bleuler was the Director there. At the turn of the century he studied at Janet's clinic in Paris. For a while he was interested in hypnosis, and he is stated to have had a concern about spiritualism and psychic research from his student days (1). He became interested in word-association studies. Evaluations of the mental functioning of normal and abnormal subjects were possible in these investigations. He noted also some relationships between the nature of dreams and the speech of certain schizophrenic patients. In 1907 he visited Vienna and met Freud. It has been said that he called Freud's attention to the Schreber autobiography (1). In 1913, Jung presented the terms and concepts of extraversion and introversion.

Lewis expresses the view that Jung was never content with the basic sexual theories proposed by Freud, and that he was more concerned with ego functioning and spiritual components in personality make-up (2). Furthermore, he was anxious to evaluate the racial or archaic elements in unconscious mental functioning and its expressions. The idea of a collective unconscious is closely identified with Jung's contributions. Lewis is of the impression that the criticism of Jung for mystical views is probably not warranted but it is well known of course that such criticism is indeed widespread.

Jung was quite interested in schizophrenia whereas Freud's major contributions have been more readily adapted to an understanding of the neuroses. When the break with Freud occurred during the second decade of this century, several issues were probably at work. Disregarding what may have been essentially personal considerations, there were, according to one observer, the basically medical tradition in his background, a Protestant religious imprint derived from his father, influences of Bleuler and Janet, special concern with the psychoses, and the influence of experimental and clinical psychology. These elements influenced his new direction (1). It seems that at mid-century an apparently limited following of Jung is by no means consistent with the world renown of the man himself. It is of interest to note the personal suggestion of the historian Arnold Toynbee that Jung has supplied a new dimension to history through the studies he has completed and made available (3). As a final item it may be essentially correct to point out that probably most psychiatrists are less familiar with the details of Jung's work than they are with the contributions of others who deviated from the mainstream of the Freudian tradition.

The second deviant group during this second decade was spearheaded by Alfred Adler (1870-1937). Adler was particularly curious about general feelings of inferiority and ideas of organ inferiority (4). He was intent on investigating strivings for superiority and described what was referred to as the masculine protest in women. The drive toward power impressed him in its various expressions. He was greatly involved in the problems of children. His work has at times been regarded as too philosophical (2). Adler's contributions seemed to move into the background for a time but in the past few years they appear to be gaining increasing attention (11). Regardless of possible disagreement, Robert W. White, as one example, has proposed that it was Adler who took the first pioneering direction toward an ego psychology within the framework of the psychoanalytic system. Details on this score have been outlined and elaborated in many clinical writings. Ardent supporters have proposed that so-called neo-Freudians in present day contexts should, indeed, be more properly called neo-Adlerians (6). Whereas the label of Analytical Psychology is generally applied to the Jungian divergence from the Freudian base, the expression Individual Psychology is applied to the Adlerian separation. Attempts have been made to correlate aspects of Adler's theories with his background and personality (75). Such studies are often of interest in connection with well known figures.

In some circles much is said about the influence of Adler on views presented by Karen Horney (1885-1953) who was the leading figure in still another psychoanalytic faction. She had recognized the claims of a link between some of her propositions and Adlerian concepts but asserted, in one of her earlier works, that despite some similarities, her interpretations rested fundamentally on Freudian grounds. She regarded Adler's ideas as rather one-sided (7). Yet it has been said that after several years of additional work on her own ideas, the debt to Adler was finally acknowledged (8). In her writings, one is often impressed by stress on the fact that Freud's outlook was essentially pessimistic whereas her own was optimistic. The many details of her contributions display keen observations of neurotic functioning and a keynote of her view of neurosis is often indicated by the expression, the struggle toward self-realization. Time will be required for an adequate appraisal of her endeavors (9).

There have, of course, been other deviations from the traditional Freudian movement. At present, one of the better known is the following of the esteemed psychiatrist, Harry Stack Sullivan (1892-1949), and the core idea of the trend associated with his studies pertains to the fundamental importance of interpersonal relations and the disturbances in this area in their influence on neurotic development (12). A minute examination of the central themes in this and other points of view would be more relevant to a history of psychoanalysis rather than to the broader field of psychiatry. Any such examination would result of necessity in disproportionate emphasis within the over-all view of the history of psychiatry if only because of the proximity of these happenings. Earlier separations can be, and have been enlarged on in specialized works. Here it is pertinent to make brief reference to Wilhelm Stekel and Otto Rank, if two well known examples were to be selected. Stekel (1868-1940) was concerned with shortening the length of treatment. He was an intuitive therapist and had interests in the psychology of homosexuality, anxiety, and epilepsy (2). His autobiography has been edited and made available (10). Rank was especially concerned with the crucial importance of birth trauma in its influence on normal and abnormal personality functioning. This emphasis has been cited as an excellent example of the role of a dominant idea and its impact on views of human behavior in all its complex manifestations.

Adolf Meyer (1866-1950) is mentioned frequently as the leading psychiatrist in the United States during the first half of this century. He arrived in 1892. He had been born in Zurich. He served as pathologist in mental hospitals at Kankakee and Worcester before becoming Director of the New York State Psychiatric Institute. From 1910 to 1941 he served as Professor of Psychiatry at the Johns Hopkins University (13). In his thinking about psychiatric illness, Meyer took into consideration biological, historical, social, and psychological elements. Such illness for him consisted of "reaction types" rather than "disease." His technical terminology involved "ergasias", but the classification scheme was short-lived. The "common sense" concept is linked to his psychiatric method, and this designation was evidently his own (14). For Meyer, the life history of the patient was important in any study of personality development. Schizophrenia was seen as the outcome of progressive maladjustment with poor adaptations and uneven personality growth (15).

The early growth and expansion of the mental hygiene movement took place early in this century and the name associated with it historically is Clifford Whittingham Beers. His autobiography may perhaps have been the most widely read of this era (16). Adolf Meyer evidently suggested that the term "mental hygiene" be applied to this development (17). Although another famed Baltimore figure of that time, William H. Welch (18), with his background in pathology and his broad view of the medical scene was also connected with the mental hygiene movement to some degree, it is of interest to note a letter from Meyer to neurosurgeon Harvey Cushing in this connection (19). In it he mentions that the "Welch school of medicine" had no sympathy for anything beyond what could be studied with its usual techniques of viewing "outside factors." He points out that there is a field of pathology in which such factors are not very tangible and manageable. Also much attention must be paid to the individual patient.

Meyer was of influence in the development of psychiatric education in medical schools although outstanding growth in such curricula has occurred more only in recent years (20). He also exerted favorable influence on hospital organization. Compared to other contributors, his literary output was not especially large, but his personal leadership and teaching promoted the point of view which he called "psychobiology" (13). In this psychobiological scheme, structural and psychological factors are fused in a searching investigation of the total patient. Its stress is on a holistic orientation. The patient is seen as a unitary, functioning individual within his social matrix.

Zilboorg has referred to Adolf Meyer as the strongest link between the medical psychology of Europe and America (13). Other well known personalities should be noted in this connection. One, for example, is Smith Ely Jeliffe (1866-1945) who has been called the Father of American Psychosomatic Medicine (21). For many years Jeliffe was editor of the *Journal of Nervous and Mental Disease* and of the *Psychoanalytic Review*. He was much involved in the integration of psychoanalytic concepts with a dynamic psychiatry. His co-editor, a distinguished psychiatrist, was William Alanson White. He was at the forefront in the development of American psychiatry during this century and served for many years as Superintendent of Saint Elizabeths Hospital in Washington. From White also we have an autobiographical work dealing with his activities and ideals (22). His efforts and abilities enabled him to get along with psychiatrists of divergent thought and practice. His personal attributes placed him in a position of acknowledged leadership in the profession (21). White's *Outlines of Psychiatry,* first published in 1908, went through many editions attesting to a most favorable reception (23).

A rather unique personality was Paul Schilder (1886-1940) who was concerned with many important aspects of psychology and psychiatry. Zilboorg credits him as the first to attempt to develop somewhat systematically a psychoanalytic psychiatry. Whitehorn regards Schilder's special contribution to be the "body image" concept (24). It was A. A. Brill, on the other hand, who is identified so very closely with the early stages of psychoanalysis. Of him it is claimed that he above all was responsible for introducing psychoanalysis into the United States. He translated many of Freud's writings into English. In this context, reference should be made also to the Swiss psychiatrist, Hermann Rorschach (1884-1922). He devised the projective test procedure which bears his name and which has come into extensive use for personality evaluation (25). At mid-century it is one of the most prominent testing devices among the several employed by clinical psychologists. An enormous literature has developed on the "Rorschach" test alone. Consistent with the theme of acceptance and non-acceptance of new ideas at home and abroad, it is of interest to note that between 1922 and 1935 no communication on the Rorschach procedure was delivered before the Swiss Psychiatric Society (25). Interest in it reached a high level by 1940.

It is evident that the first half of the twentieth century saw important strides in the development of psychological theory and practice in psychiatry. At the same time certain innovations were introduced which had to do with a physiological approach in treatment methods. Outstanding in this respect was the introduction by Manfred Sakel (1900-1957) of insulin shock therapy for schizophrenia in 1927. It had great impact on the hospital practice of psychiatry although, as could be expected, many differences of opinion regarding its efficacy were verbalized. Furthermore, as is the case usually with newly introduced methods, modifications were developed. On the one hand claims are made for the greater effectiveness of such modifications. On the other, adherents to classical or traditional procedures stress the necessity for use of the original techniques. As for the results claimed or achieved, there is some reason to believe that what the innovators bring technically and psychologically to their therapeutic endeavors has important implications. These implications relate to both excessive claims and truly effective achievement.

Sakel's insulin shock treatment has been considered by some a milestone in the advancement of psychiatry (26). Hans Hoff states that it supplied the impetus for the introduction of the physiological measures that followed in the form of electric and metrazol shock in the treatment of mental illness. The atmosphere of despair in psychiatric hospitals was thus favorably affected. As a tribute to Sakel it was noted that in Vienna of the 1950s, the "classical procedure" was still retained. Others have ventured to call this method the first successful treatment of schizophrenia, an assertion which would not be supported by all (27). Sakel was born in Poland at a location which was then part of the Austro-Hungarian Empire. When in Berlin he observed the resemblance between certain withdrawal symptoms in abstinence cures of morphine addicts, and manifestations of hyperthyroidism. He used insulin as a thyroid antagonist, discovered helpful effects of hypoglycemic insulin shock, experimented further and noted its benefits in schizophrenia (27).

The use of electric shock therapy a few years later was found to be particularly effective with some types of depressions. Despite differences of opinion regarding its efficacy or desirability, the fact remains that electroconvulsive treatment and various modifications of it have been used widely and have in many cases reduced the severity of depressions or the length of time the depressions have persisted. Questions have come up regarding theoretical issues, the problem of recurrences, and the concern about failure so often to incorporate psychotherapeutic measures for the purpose of helping the patient to reach a degree of greater stability than would be implied in symptomatic change alone. These and other issues are not elaborated now. They are meaningful as present day concerns but much too close for historical evaluation. This applies also to other therapeutic measures in the treatment of the neuroses and psychoses which are categorized as "physiological." At this time, just beyond the half century mark, pharmacotherapy has come into great prominence with a large variety of medications used for reduction of anxiety and diminution in the intensity of neurotic and psychotic symptoms. For the reasons stated, details must await future evaluation. Again, points of view differ in regard to the widespread use of such medications, many of which are accompanied by the popular designation, "tranquilizers." As far as many hospital administrators are concerned, an important observation is the increased discharge rate from large state institutions. Conservative appraisals of new therapeutic measures are warranted and require the passage of time. There is always the risk of reviving the cult of curability which existed for a while in the nineteenth century.

Among the treatment methods which do not subscribe to a basically psychological approach to the patient, though striving to benefit their psychological functioning, are the psychosurgical techniques. In 1936 Egas Moniz, a neurologist of Lisbon, Portugal, in collaboration with the surgeon, Almeida Lima, performed an operation of the frontal lobes of a group of patients and initiated leukotomy (28). It was only after the spread of psychosurgical procedures in the United States that such techniques became more firmly implanted in the psychiatric scene, and a variety of experimental explorations followed with diversified means of destroying, in one way or another, several areas of brain structure (30). The irreversibility of the effects produced played an important role in the hesitancy of some psychiatrists to regard these methods in a favorable light, accompanied by the usual disagreements regarding the benefit derived or the harm really produced. This work continues while psychological studies are done on the patients, and the main interest in these measures is found largely among psychiatrists who would be described as oriented neurologically. Criticism is most pronounced among therapists who favor psychological techniques with psychiatric problems, but severe condemnation stems from other sources too (29). If chemotherapeutic efforts bear significant fruit in the future, this may perhaps in some way lead to a lessening in surgical endeavors.

The psychosurgical procedures are, of course, only the most recent in a series of measures used through the years in attacking the problem of mental illness. At the very beginnings of such concerns, the trepanation methods were part of the magico-religious systems. Yet only a decade prior to the destruction of brain tissue for relief of mental affliction, Henry Cotton, in the United States, starting about 1922, centered attention on focal infection in its etiological role for mental illness. He favored removal of teeth, tonsils, and then colons. Casamajor claimed that one of its achievements at least was the encouragement of some interest on the part of doctors in mental disease (31). It is important to be aware, in connection with any efforts to relieve mental distress, that everything done with and to patients has its psychological implications for them and induces some effects. It is difficult to evaluate therapeutic change for this reason, insofar as attempts to relate cause and effect are concerned. At present this is pointed up especially in the case of the chemotherapeutic agents. Carefully controlled studies with chemically relevant and inert agents demonstrate changes in the direction of relief for the patients, to varying degrees, and it is clear that factors affecting change relate not only to the medicine prescribed but to the circumstances surrounding its administration, the doctor-patient relationship and the attitudes involved, and a variety of complex, allied issues and circumstances.

The several physical, physiological and chemical interests in mental illness with their obvious dependency on knowledge of brain structure and fine anatomical detail call to mind those investigators responsible for expanding knowledge about the tissue substrate. It is not necessary to go into detail about this background, but if any one name were to be singled out for special attention it may well be Santiago Ramon y Cajal. Some of his work related to the direction of nerve-currents in brain and spinal cord and the nature of the contact between nerve cells. Regarding the larger expanse of his contribution, Sir Charles Sherrington commented that in a period of six short years he changed, single-handed, the study of functional anatomy of the vertebrate nervous system. He asked whether Cajal might not indeed be the greatest anatomist of the nervous system (32). Yet a good thing can be stretched too far, and the assertion of Cajal's biographer that to a considerable degree his work made modern neuropsychiatry possible is not really consistent with our knowledge of present day psychiatry (33).

The changes in psychiatric points of view and treatment methods are varied and it is possible to trace the developments through records in the confines of individual hospitals. This fact is appreciated by some (34). At the same time there comes to light not only the step by step advances or recessions but intuitive predictions. The neuropathological laboratory was an established unit in many locations at the turn of the century. But in 1907, in an annual report of Saint Elizabeths Hospital, William A. White focussed attention on the establishment of a psychological department which he considered one of the most advanced trends in psychiatry at that time. He predicted its necessity thereafter as part of the structure of a psychiatric unit, as the pathological laboratory had been up until then (35). In the meantime, speaking in another vein, the clinician had his own bedside laboratory when we take into consideration the major problem of psychiatry in the past and now. Zilboorg tells us with reference to the outstanding psychiatrist Thomas W. Salmon (1876-1927), that he would mention syphilis referred to as the experimental laboratory for clinical medicine and add that schizophrenia might be regarded as the experimental laboratory of clinical psychopathology (36, 37).

A major development in recent decades has been the growth of the field of social work with special reference to psychiatric social work. The concept itself, Deutsch tell us, was first introduced with the publication of *The Kingdom of Evils* in 1922 by Elmer E. Southard (1876-1920) and social worker Mary C. Jarrett (38). Psychiatric social work has placed its imprint not only on the functioning of clinics and hospitals but on the broader expanse of entire communities coming face to face with the great issue of mental health. Southard of Harvard brought his influence to a group of active students who still pay him homage, one of whom points out that this influential figure, though a pathologist, strongly combatted the anti-psychologism of the time (21). The impetus for the psychiatric social work movement apparently stemmed from the World War I emergency, for it was then that a course of lectures on psychiatry was given to social workers at Smith College. Southard was Director of the Boston Psychopathic Hospital (28).

Karl Menninger, one of Southard's pupils, has mentioned his influence often. He tells of Southard as the inspiration for his book, *The Human Mind* (39), originally prepared for professional readers but seeming to attract the layman even more (21). Mention of this possesses more than passing interest, because the twentieth century has seen a remarkable attraction on the part of the general public to popular literature of many forms dealing with psychiatric and psychological material. Part of this is undoubtedly a healthy attempt at education in an area of new awareness and importance. Part is probably an expression of confusion and ambivalent attitudes toward the varied assertions and declarations of vocal components of the psychiatric and psychological professions. Regardless of this mixed picture, and amidst a profuse outpouring of questionable printed material, books such as the one mentioned have a significant place in the advance of medical ideas within the profession itself and among the more informed segments of the general public. Fortunately there are a number of good books which stand apart from the sea of mediocrity. They, along with the authors, are too many to mention, but it should be noted that leaders of the profession have played a role in their publication. One pertinent example is Edward A. Strecker (1886-1959), co-author of *Discovering Ourselves,* educator, and a President of the American Psychiatric Association (40).

Among the good books inviting the attention of the general public are some highlighting what has come to be widely called "dynamic psychiatry." Never precisely defined, as Lowrey pointed out, its usage began to spread from about 1915 (41). The term "psychiatry" had been used before the middle of the nineteenth century. By 1895 it was quite common. The word "alienist" was especially acceptable during the second part of the nineteenth century (31).

The past few decades have witnessed great intensification of interest in the psychological problems of children and the rapid growth of Child Psychiatry as a sub-specialty. Lawson G. Lowrey was much interested in its historical development (42). This began with care and training of mental defectives, said to be the only psychiatric endeavors with reference to children from 1846 to 1909 approximately. At the same time, however, there was concern with "child study" and stress on education. From 1909 to 1919 attention was turned to children and the problem of delinquency. The Chicago Juvenile Psychopathic Institute was founded in 1909 by William Healy and it pioneered in the area of child guidance clinics (38). It is rated the first clinic for children incorporating psychiatric, psychological, and social approaches. Nevertheless, mention should be made of the Psychological Clinic established in 1896 at the University of Pennsylvania by Lightner Witmer. After 1919 there was rapid development of child guidance clinics, inpatient and outpatient services in psychopathic, state, and general hospitals, and a variety of schools and institutions ministering to the needs of children with psychiatric disabilities. It seemed that stress was largely on psychopathology, but in some locations intensive studies of normal development were emphasized, and this field of knowledge has had its outstanding representatives (43).

While the aforementioned developments were taking place, gradual unifications were attempted, in clinical and experimental investigations, between psychiatry with its new insights and other medical specialties. Some internists showed more interest in, and awareness of psychological implications and expressions of illness than did others. Lewellys Barker told of his interest in psychotherapy, and of his propagating views on its importance (50). He pointed out that his predecessor in Baltimore, William Osler, had really been more interested in "organic" than in "functional" disorders of the nervous system, consistent with his pathological-anatomical rather than pathological-physiological background (51). The unfortunate separation of medicine and surgery centuries ago was stressed by the medical historian Fielding H. Garrison (44, 45) and the outstanding British physician, Sir Clifford Albutt (46). Many physicians believe a similar threat has existed in the separation of psychiatry from medicine.

As has been mentioned earlier, as far as "pyschosomatic medicine" is concerned, the term had been introduced during the early part of the last century, but it came into special prominence after 1935 (47, 48). It has been considered of questionable desirability because it implies a dichotomy that is inconsistent with the clear desire to emphasize a holistic concept of functioning. This is obvious and there is no need to continue the tiresome condemnation. More important is the assertion, as voiced by Stanley Cobb, that many psychiatrists supply only lip service to a monistic concept of the human organism with persistent adherence in their thinking to dualistic views (49). He is undoubtedly correct in pointing out the difficulty in eliminating patterns of thought that date back to the distant past. He has encouraged the conception of health and illness as reactions of the organism to a complex internal and external environment. Tribute was paid to Walter B. Cannon for his investigations into the physiology of the emotions (52). Cobb has expressed the opinion that present day psychosomatic medicine is a reaction against the emphasis on laboratory medicine during the second half of the nineteenth century (53).

In the past few decades there have been many variations in emphasis within the field of theory, practice, and teaching of psychotherapy. Forms of group therapy have come to be widely used. The term "group psychotherapy" is believed to have appeared first only in 1931 (54). The modern beginnings are often dated back to the turn of this century when the internist, Joseph H. Pratt worked with groups of patients to assist with their emotional problems connected with tuberculosis. It may have been a time saving factor that was considered initially to be of essential importance, followed later by greater awareness of psychological benefits. After the first World War, William Alanson White encouraged group therapy investigations, and Paul Schilder, among others, was interested in psychoanalytically oriented group therapy (55).

The periodic revival and recession of interest in hypnotic techniques is reflected in the history of psychiatry. Concern with brief therapy invariably arises during wartime, and both World Wars have, as a result, seen renewed involvements with hypnotic methods for psychiatric disability. Their applicability for longer term as well as short term treatment has been more greatly appreciated only recently. In the last major war, the measures labelled narcoanalysis and narcosynthesis were mentioned prominently although hypnotherapy was also employed (74). Familiarity with mechanical injection and use of drugs probably was important in this connection, and the measures were easier to teach and to be learned by physicians who had to be prepared rapidly for emergency situations (56). After the war came to an end, continued interest in, and the scientific development of clinical and experimental hypnosis was furthered by the organization of scientific workers seriously concerned with the complex aspects of this field for study of personality functioning (57). The rise and growth of medical specialization found the field of hypnosis involved in concurrent integration, and the first textbook dealing with hypnosis and the medical specialties was published (58). Psychiatric hypnotherapy kept pace with the expansion of dynamic psychiatry, and hypnoanalysis came into being as an amalgamation of old and new hypnotic techniques with classical and neo-Freudian theoretical psychoanalytic concepts (Schneck, 59). The recurrent focus on special committees or commissions for authoritative statements regarding hypnosis came to expression again as recently as mid-century with the favorable official statements of the British Medical Association in 1955 and the American Medical Association in 1958.

Involved in the developmental trends of psychiatry have been an increasing number of psychologists. The field of psychology has grown enormously and clinical psychologists in particular have become more and more a part of psychiatric clinical and research activities. In hospitals and clinics they have served with psychiatrists and social workers as part of what is often referred to as a "team" effort. Since World War II, many psychologists have entered the private practice of psychotherapy. The private practice of psychiatry has, of course, expanded greatly, and the reason often given for the need of service on the part of psychologists is the great demand for psychotherapy by the general public. There are involved problems in this regard, and an attempt will not be made to supply details because they are so much a part of the contemporary scene which cannot be seen fairly from the vantage point of history. Suffice it to say that one of the main objections to the practice of psychotherapy without clearly defined medical supervision is that the practice of psychotherapy is basically the practice of medicine, and that it cannot be separated from such practice. To do so, it is felt, would unquestionably constitute a retrogression in medical procedure, and would inhibit healthy expansion of psychiatry in particular. The way in which this issue will be resolved eventually is not apparent as yet. It should be pointed out, however, that many contributions have been supplied by psychologists that are meaningful to psychiatry, and, as is the case with psychiatry itself, an enormous literature has been produced. Some volumes are more helpful than others in supplying a good view of these contributions because they possess broad coverage and significant detail (60).

The aforementioned literary output is so vast indeed, that it has become almost an insurmountable problem for the individual practitioner to keep well informed in the area of his own sub-specialty, no less the over-all field of psychiatry or the broader field of medicine. In the area of psychotherapy alone, points of view and methods in practice are manifold. Unfortunately, misunderstandings arise frequently and are complicated by difficulties in what is now so fashionably-called "communication." As for some reasonable attempt to assess the more outstanding contributions to psychotherapy in its developments during the first half of this century, reference may be made to the volume by Werner Wolff in the production of which he interviewed outstanding representatives of several schools of thought and practice (62).

Difficult as it is with the rapid growth of psychiatry in the twentieth century to assess developments in the one area of psychotherapy, it can be imagined how great is the problem of dealing with the entire specialty. At mid-century an attempt to approach some view of psychiatric treatment was made under the auspices of the Association for Research in Nervous and Mental Disease. Psychological, social, pharmacological, electrical, and neurosurgical procedures were taken into consideration with recognition of the fact that therapy must encompass not only the individual, but his own family and his social environment. As S. Bernard Wortis pointed out, critical evaluations of treatment had to be attempted with an assessment of basic factors, methods, and utility. Quite properly the claim was made that the therapist should exercise humility in voicing his views on exclusive efficacy of any one treatment method. Also, there was repeated what has been said on a number of occasions about treatment results at this time. It appeared that about one-third of patients do not respond to treatment, one-third get well under treatment, and the remaining one-third are assisted to some extent. Furthermore, relatively little information was available about what happened to patients who remained untreated (62).

The many special subdivisions of treatment in psychiatry and stress on the contributions of ancillary services have found representation in separate professional journals, books, and other writings. Their magnitude is considerable. Aside from the professional field of psychiatric nursing one need focus only on the acknowledged, major role of occupational therapy in all its complexity. The latter has been done by William Rush Dunton, Jr. and presented with his co-author in a volume containing an account of the historical development of this treatment approach. Credit is given George Edward Barton for originating the term "occupational therapy" shortly after the turn of the century.

Increasing emphasis on the social aspects of psychiatry has, as a matter of fact, given rise to the term, "social psychiatry", but Thomas Rennie indicated that surely this does not imply a new kind of psychiatry (63). Rather, it signifies a broadening emphasis on the contributions of psychiatrists, sociologists and anthropologists concerned with their interrelated problems and the bearing of their disciplines on issues of psychiatric assistance and understanding. Many works have been issued to emphasize and illustrate the cross-disciplinary view that is a constantly growing feature of present day psychiatric study (64). The importance of related disciplines, for greater understanding of the development and functioning of man as an individual and as part of his social community is obvious. Within the more special and structured context of the doctor-patient relationship, too, the cultural matrix affects each in terms of acquired orientation to disease, treatment and cure (65).

Taking the social and cultural milieu into consideration, we are bound to consider again the legal aspects of psychiatry. Once more, and with perhaps greater gravity than ever before, the problems of man and his conflicts with society are calling for much needed attention. Attempts to cope with the difficult issues of psychiatry and the law have barely scratched the surface. Today, the outmoded M'Naughten rules of 1843 still reign, but what is to replace them? On this, there is no general agreement. An element of hope was discerned by Justice William O. Douglas when he commented on the 1954 case of Durham v. United States decided by the Court of Appeals for the District of Columbia. The "right or wrong" and "irresistible impulse" tests of insanity as defense in criminal cases were replaced by the assertion that an accused does not bear criminal responsibility for an unlawful act that is the product of mental disease or mental defect. This was considered by many to be more in keeping with modern medical and psychiatric thought (66). Further developments in this attempted break with traditional opinion have yet to be observed.

At the same time that efforts have been made to further understandings between the legal and medical professions, movements have been initiated to bring clergymen and psychiatrists into closer rapport and to study the involved relationships between religion and mental health (67).

While interest in man from a scientific point of view has been growing constantly, this view has incorporated increasingly the issues of moral and ethical values. Part of this reaching out in many directions for better understanding has been the emergence in the field of psychiatry of what has been labelled an "existential analytic" approach (68). This development appears to have made more significant strides on the European scene than on the American. Some of those much impressed with it consider its ingredients to be consistent with basic elements in psychoanalysis. Others declare that there is essential incompatibility between the two (69). What the historical implications will be cannot possibly be guessed now.

The status of psychiatry varies much in countries throughout the world. Even if technical measures are disregarded, the fundamental involvement with mental health in its broadest considerations differs considerably in different areas. Apparent progress may be followed by lag, and at times there is tragic retrogression. Not very long ago, psychiatric thinking identified with the western world began to make some impression in China. In 1897 the first mental hospital for thirty patients was opened in Canton. It expanded in forty years to accommodate 500 patients, but this institution and a few others that came into being could not withstand the devastating impact of the Second World War. They went out of existence (70). But in the years that followed, American medicine and the specialty of psychiatry appeared to be exerting an ever increasing influence in many countries (71).

Yet, as James B. Conant, a leading scientist and educator, has said, in the practical application of sciences dealing with human behavior there is a very high degree of empiricism. At mid-century he was inclined to point out that the future looked promising, but psychologists and anthropologists must admit that the conceptual schemes available to them were the equivalent of what chemists and physicists possessed in the late eighteenth century (72).

It is always a temptation to guess the future. As the sixth decade neared its close, Franz Alexander ventured to say, "We live in an era of collaboration and integration. The solitary man of the nineteenth century, with his impregnable self-sufficient system of values, is rapidly yielding his place to the communal, the so-called other-directed person with a soul, searching vainly for his own identity. The imprint of this cultural shift upon psychiatry manifests itself in the growing interest in group dynamics and its sociologic aspects. In this light I see the developments of the next ten years in a growing integration of the biologic, psychodynamic and sociologic approaches, and the emergence of a comprehensive psychiatry which no longer attempts to solve the great mystery of human behavior from one single restricted point of view but, in each approach, trying to enrich itself by considering rather than disregarding, or minimizing, the contributions coming from the other avenues of research."

Commenting on the history of science, Sir William Cecil Dampier made the frequently encountered observation that its description stresses accounts of successes, and theories that tend to survive at least for a time. This results in a misleading impression of a steady series of triumphs. Yet, in fact there are many failures and they match the number of successes "inscribed on the role of fame" (73). The development of psychiatry reflects advances and retrogressions, periods of relative light and relative darkness. The evaluations of such periods undergo change to a lesser or greater degree from time to time. This is bound to happen because so much depends on perspective. Such perspective, in turn, is conditioned by leading opinions and fashions of the time. To rise above the tides and pressures of contemporary conformity is no easy task. One is justified, nevertheless, in having faith that in the years to come psychiatry will continue to play a fundamental role in the healing art of medicine and in the scientific study of nature and the search for truth. Precisely what the future holds in store remains to be seen . . .

REFERENCES

1. Clark, R. A.: Jung and Freud, A Chapter in Psychoanalytic History. *Am. J. Psychoth., 9*:605, 1955.
2. Lewis, N. D. C.: *A Short History of Psychiatric Achievement.* London, Chapman and Hall, 1942.
3. Toynbee, A.: The Value of C. G. Jung's Work for Historians. *J. Anal. Psychol., 1*:193, 1956.
4. Bottome, P.: *Alfred Adler.* New York, G. P. Putnam's Sons, 1939.
5. White, R. W.: Adler and the Future of Ego Psychology. *J. Individual Psychol., 13*:112, 1957.
6. Ansbacher, H. L. and R. R.: *The Individual Psychology of Alfred Adler.* New York, Basic Books, 1956.
7. Horney, K.: *The Neurotic Personality of Our Time.* New York, W. W. Norton, 1937.
8. White, R. W.: Is Alfred Adler Alive Today? *Contemporary Psychol., 2*:1, 1957.
9. Horney, K.: *Neurosis and Human Growth.* New York, W. W. Norton, 1950.
10. Stekel, W.: *The Autobiography of Wilhelm Stekel* (Edited by E. A. Gutheil). New York, Liveright, 1950.
11. Adler, A.: *What Life Should Mean To You.* New York, Grosset and Dunlap, 1931.
12. Sullivan, H. S.: *Conceptions of Modern Psychiatry.* Washington, William Alanson White Psychiatric Foundation, 1947.
13. Zilboorg, G. and Henry, G. W.: *A History of Medical Psychology.* New York, W. W. Norton, 1941.
14. Szasz, T. S.: The Problems of Psychiatric Nosology. *Am. J. Psychiat., 114*:405, 1957.
15. Wall, J. H.: Problems In Schizophrenia. *N. Y. State J. Med., 56*:2864, 1956.
16. Beers, C. W.: *A Mind That Found Itself* (2nd Edition). New York, Longmans, 1910.
17. Winkler, J. K. and Bromberg, W.: *Mind Explorers.* New York, Reynal and Hitchcock, 1939.
18. Fleming, D.: *William H. Welch and the Rise of Modern Medicine.* Boston, Little, Brown and Company, 1954.

19. Fulton, J. F.: *Harvey Cushing.* Springfield, Thomas, 1946.
20. Barta, F. R.: A Brief History of Psychiatric Education at the Creighton University School of Medicine. *Nebraska State Med. J., 39*:280, 1954.
21. Menninger, K. A.: Freud and American Psychiatry. *J. Am. Psychoanal. Assn., 14*:614, 1956.
22. White, W. A.: *The Autobiography of a Purpose.* New York, Doubleday, Doran, 1938.
23. Lewis, N. D. C.: *Review of the Scientific Publications From Saint Elizabeths Hospital During the Past 100 Years (Centennial Papers).* Washington, Saint Elizabeths Hospital, 1956.
24. Whitehorn, J. C.: A Century of Psychiatric Research In America. In Hall, J. K.: *One Hundred Years of American Psychiatry.* New York, Columbia University Press, 1944.
25. Ellenberger, H.: The Life and Work of Hermann Rorschach (1884-1922). *Bull. Menninger Clinic, 18*:173, 1954.
26. Hoff, H.: Forward to Sakel, M.: *Schizophrenia.* New York, Philosophical Library, 1958.
27. Wortis, J.: Manfred Sakel, M.D., 1900-1957. *Am. J. Psychiat., 115*:287, 1958.
28. Bromberg, W.: *Man Above Humanity.* Philadelphia, J. B. Lippincott, 1954.
29. Bailey, P.: The Great Psychiatric Revolution. *Am. J. Psychiat., 113*:387, 1956.
30. Freeman, W. and Watts, J. W.: *Psychosurgery in the Treatment of Mental Disorders and Intractable Pain.* Springfield, Thomas, 1950.
31. Casamajor, L.: Notes for an Intimate History of Neurology and Psychiatry in America. *J. Nerv. and Ment. Dis., 98*:600, 1943.
32. Sherrington, C.: A Memoir of Dr. Cajal. In Cannon, D. F.: *Explorer of the Human Brain.* New York, Henry Schuman, 1949.
33. Cannon, D. F.: *Explorer of the Human Brain, The Life of Santiago Ramon y Cajal.* New York, Henry Schuman, 1949.
34. Warner, J. D. and Moss, C. S.: A Century of Medical Treatment at State Hospital No. 1, An Historical Perspective. *Am. Psychol., 13*:120, 1958.
35. Ives, M.: Fifty Years of Hospital Psychology. *Am. Psychol., 12*:150, 1957.
36. Zilboorg, G.: The Problem of Ambulatory Schizophrenia. *Am. J.*

Psychiat., *113*:519, 1956.

37. Bond, E. D.: *Thomas W. Salmon, Psychiatrist.* New York, W. W. Norton, 1950.
38. Deutsch, A.: The History of Mental Hygiene. In Hall, J. K.: *One Hundred Years of American Psychiatry.* New York, Columbia University Press, 1944.
39. Menninger, K. A.: *The Human Mind.* New York, Alfred A. Knopf, 1930.
40. Bond, E. D.: Edward A. Strecker, M.D., 1886-1959. *Am. J. Psychiat.*, *115*:959, 1959.
41. Lowrey, L. G.: The Contribution of Orthopsychiatry to Psychiatry: Brief Historical Note. *Am. J. Orthopsychiat.*, *25*:475, 1955.
42. Lowrey, L. G.: Psychiatry for Children, A Brief History of Developments. *Am. J. Psychiat.*, *101*:375, 1944.
43. Gesell, A.: Autobiography. In Langfeld, H. S., Boring, E. G., Werner, H. and Yerkes, R. M.: *A History of Psychology In Autobiography* (Vol. 4). Worcester, Mass., Clark University Press, 1952.
44. Garrison, F. H.: *Introduction to the History of Medicine.* Philadelphia, Saunders, 1929.
45. Kagan, S. R.: *Life and Letters of Fielding H. Garrison.* Boston, Medico-Historical Press, 1938.
46. Rolleston, H. D.: *The Life of Sir Thomas Clifford Albutt.* London, Macmillan, 1929.
47. Weiss, E.: The Origins of Psychosomatic Medicine. *Phila. Med.*, *52*:620, 1956.
48. Dunbar, H. F.: *Emotions and Bodily Changes, A Survey of Literature on Psychosomatic Interrelationships.* New York, Columbia University Press, 1935.
49. Cobb, S.: Monism and Psychosomatic Medicine. *Psychosomatic Med.*, *19*:177, 1957.
50. Barker, L. F.: *Time and the Physician.* New York, G. P. Putnam's Sons, 1942.
51. Cushing, H.: *The Life of Sir William Osler.* New York, Oxford University Press, 1925.
52. Cannon, W. B.: *Bodily Changes in Pain, Hunger, Fear and Rage.* New York, D. Appleton and Company, 1929.
53. Cobb, S.: One Hundred Years of Progress in Neurology, Psychiatry and Neurosurgery. *Arch. Neurol. and Psychiat.*, *59*:63, 1948.
54. Corsini, R. J.: Historic Background of Group Psychotherapy: A

Critique. *Group Psychotherap.*, *3*:219, 1955.

55. Hadden, S. B.: Historic Background of Group Psychotherapy. *Int. J. Group Psychotherap.*, *5*:162, 1955.
56. Grinker, R. R. and Spiegel, J. P.: *War Neuroses in North Africa.* New York, Josiah Macy, Jr. Foundation, 1943.
57. Schneck, J. M.: An Outline of the Development of the Society for Clinical and Experimental Hypnosis. *J. Clin. Exper. Hyp.*, *1*:2, 1953.
58. Schneck, J. M.: *Hypnosis in Modern Medicine* (Second Edition). Springfield, Thomas, 1959.
59. Schneck, J. M.: *Studies In Scientific Hypnosis.* Baltimore, Williams and Wilkins, 1954.
60. Brower, D. and Abt, L. E.: *Progress in Clinical Psychology* (Vol. 2). New York, Grune and Stratton, 1956.
61. Wolff, W.: *Contemporary Psychotherapists Examine Themselves.* Springfield, Thomas, 1956.
62. Wortis, S. B. (Ed.): *Psychiatric Treatment.* Baltimore, Williams and Wilkins, 1953.
63. Opler, M. K.: Cultural Anthropology and Social Psychiatry. *Am. J. Psychiat.*, *113*:302, 1956.
64. Kluckhohn, C. and Murray, H. A. (Editors): *Personality in Nature, Society, and Culture.* New York, Alfred A. Knopf, 1948.
65. Szasz, T. S., Knoff, W. F. and Hollender, M. H.: The Doctor-Patient Relationship and its Historical Context. *Am. J. Psychiat.*, *115*:522, 1958.
66. Douglas, W. O.: *Law and Psychiatry.* New York, The William Alanson White Institute of Psychiatry, Psychoanalysis and Psychology, 1956.
67. Anderson, G. C.: *The Founding of the Academy.* Address delivered at the First Annual Meeting of the Board of Trustees and the Advisory Council of the National Academy of Religion and Mental Health, Princeton, New Jersey, October 19, 1956.
68. May, R., Angel, E. and Ellenberger, H.: *Existence: A New Dimension in Psychiatry and Psychology.* New York, Basic Books, 1958.
69. Schmidl, F.: Sigmund Freud and Ludwig Binswanger. *Psychoanal. Quart.*, *28*:40, 1959.
70. Veith, I.: Psychiatric Thought in Chinese Medicine. *J. Hist. Med. & Allied Sc.*, *10*:261, 1955.
71. Laughlin, H. P.: Psychiatry in Asia and the Middle East. *Am. J.*

Psychiat., 115:193, 1958.

72. Conant, J. B.: *Science and Common Sense.* New Haven, Yale University Press, 1951.
73. Dampier, W. C.: *A Shorter History of Science.* Cambridge, Cambridge University Press, 1944.
74. Raginsky, B. B.: Psychosomatic Medicine, Its History, Development and Teaching. *Am. J. Med., 5*:857, 1948.
75. Ansbacher, H. L.: The Significance of the Socio-Economic Status of the Patients of Freud and of Adler. *Am. J. Psychoth., 13*:376, 1959.

GLOSSARY OF PROFESSIONAL JOURNAL ABBREVIATIONS

American Journal of Medicine—*Am. J. Med.*
American Journal of Orthopsychiatry—*Am. J. Orthopsychiat.*
American Journal of Psychiatry—*Am. J. Psychiat.*
American Journal of Psychotherapy—*Am. J. Psychoth.*
American Journal of Surgery—*Am. J. Surg.*
American Psychologist—*Am. Psychol.*
Archives of Internal Medicine—*Arch. Int. Med.*
Archives of Neurology and Psychiatry—*Arch. Neurol. and Psychiat.*
Behavioral Science—*Behavioral Sc.*
British Journal of Medical Psychology—*Brit. J. Med. Psychol.*
British Journal of Physical Medicine—*Brit. J. Physical Med.*
British Medical Journal—*Brit. M. J.*
Bulletin of the History of Medicine—*Bull. Hist. Med.*
Bulletin of the Medical Library Association—*Bull. Med. Lib. Assn.*
Bulletin of the Menninger Clinic—*Bull. Menninger Clin.*
Ciba Symposia—*Ciba Symp.*
Contemporary Psychology—*Contemporary Psychol.*
Current Medical Digest—*Curr. Med. Dig.*
Group Psychotherapy—*Group Psychotherap.*
Guy's Hospital Reports—*Guy's Hosp. Rep.*
International Journal of Group Psychotherapy—*Int. J. Group Psychotherap.*
International Journal of Psycho-Analysis—*Int. J. Psycho-Analysis.*
International Record of Medicine and General Practice Clinics—*Int. Rec. Med. and Gen. Pract. Clin.*
Isis—*Isis.*
Journal of Abnormal and Social Psychology—*J. Abn. and Soc. Psychol.*
Journal of the American Medical Association—*J. Am. M. A.*
Journal of the American Psychoanalytic Association—*J. Am. Psychoanal. Assn.*
Journal of the American Society for Psychical Research—*J. Am. Soc. for Psychical Res.*

Journal of Analytical Psychology—*J. Anal. Psychol.*
Journal of Clinical and Experimental Hypnosis—*J. Clin. Exper. Hyp.*
Journal of Clinical and Experimental Psychopathology—*J. Clin. Exper. Psychopath.*
Journal of the History of Medicine and Allied Sciences—*J. Hist. Med. & Allied Sc.*
Journal of Individual Psychology—*J. Individual Psychol.*
Journal of Mental Science—*J. Ment. Sc.*
Journal of Nervous and Mental Disease—*J. Nerv. and Ment. Dis.*
Journal of the South Carolina Medical Association—*J. South Carolina Med. Assn.*
Lancet—*Lancet*
Medical Bookman and Historian—*Med. Bookman and Historian*
Medical History—*Med. Hist.*
Medical Press—*Med. Press*
Menninger Quarterly—*Menninger Quart.*
Mental Hygiene—*Ment. Hyg.*
Nebraska State Medical Journal—*Nebraska State Med. J.*
Neurology—*Neurology*
New England Journal of Medicine—*New Eng. J. Med.*
New York State Journal of Medicine—*N. Y. State J. Med.*
Ohio State Medical Journal—*Ohio State M. J.*
Philadelphia Medicine—*Phila. Med.*
Proceedings of the Royal Society of Medicine—*Proc. Royal Soc. Med.*
Psychoanalytic Quarterly—*Psychoanal. Quart.*
Psychoanalytic Review—*Psychoanal. Rev.*
Psychological Bulletin—*Psychol. Bull.*
Psychosomatic Medicine—*Psychosomatic Med.*
Science—*Science*
Scientific Monthly—*Sc. Monthly*
St. Bartholomew's Hospital Journal—*St. Bartholomew's Hosp. J.*
Therapeutic Notes—*Therap. Notes*
Transactions and Studies of the College of Physicians of Philadelphia—*Trans. and Studies of the Coll. Phys. Phila.*
What's New—*What's New*

AUTHOR INDEX

SUBJECT INDEX

H

I

J

K

L

M

N

Q

R

S

T

U

V